PHYSICAL ELECTRONICS

Physical Electronics

G. F. ALFREY

Department of Electron Physics
University of Birmingham

D. VAN NOSTRAND COMPANY LTD
LONDON

TORONTO   NEW YORK

PRINCETON, NEW JERSEY

D. VAN NOSTRAND COMPANY LTD
358 Kensington High Street, London, W.14

D. VAN NOSTRAND COMPANY INC.
120 Alexander Street, Princeton, New Jersey
24 West 40 Street, New York 18, New York

D. VAN NOSTRAND COMPANY (CANADA) LTD
25 Hollinger Road, Toronto 16

Library of Congress Card No. 64-22290

Printed in Great Britain by
Elliott Bros. & Yeoman Ltd, Speke, Liverpool

Preface

THIS book is an attempt to provide a concise and coherent introduction to the physical principles governing the operation of electronic devices. It is written for electrical engineers and for physicists who are interested in the way the principles of their subject are applied; pressure on the syllabus not uncommonly pushes this aspect beyond the reach of formal instruction.

Assuming some slight familiarity with the electrostatics of point charges, and with the basic principles of the electromagnetic field laid down by Maxwell, the aim is to explore the region of tension between these very different ideas—a constructive tension, as will appear. Basically, it is a matter of discussing the way in which the physicist tackles the problems arising when the electrostatic point charge finds embodiment in the electron, and their practical consequences. The space devoted to a topic reflects not so much its intrinsic importance, as the unfamiliarity of the basic ideas from which it arises.

My experience in introducing electrical engineering students to the subject indicated the need for a new kind of book. There are many excellent texts on physical electronics, but they are without exception too detailed to be completely suitable. Approaching a subject for the first time, the reader normally lacks the essential knack of seeing the wood without being distracted by the trees, and a certain amount of thinning and pruning is most desirable.

This need to be brief brings us against two limitations. The first, relatively trivial, is that many topics of potential interest have to be excluded. Since in any case comprehensiveness is impossible I have attempted instead to choose those examples which best illustrate the general development of the theme, realizing that in no event shall I please everybody.

The second limitation is more serious. The treatment is largely qualitative and it will no doubt be possible to read the book and yet be defeated by a relatively simple problem, without having acquired that feel for the numerical magnitudes of the quantities concerned which is rightly regarded as an essential part of the scientist's intellectual equipment. It is certainly not my intention to undervalue these things, but rather to suggest that they can only come later, and that algebraic and arithmetic dexterity not

5

built on a sound knowledge of the structure of the subject is not only bad but dangerous. It is this foundation which is my chief concern here.

Finally, the reader should try the problems. For the most part elementary, they may go some way towards mitigating the limitations of the text which we have just mentioned. To see what kind of *specific* questions can be asked, and to discover the difficulties involved in trying to answer them, is a good introduction to more advanced studies.

Thus while I hope many will find this book necessary, I trust that none may find it sufficient. It is merely an introduction to the books mentioned in the bibliography and the references at the ends of chapters, though I hope that it may continue to serve the reader in his more advanced studies as a kind of guide book relating his work to other aspects of a wide and expanding field.

G.F.A.

Contents

Fundamental Constants

1 eV	$= 1{\cdot}6021 \times 10^{-19}$ joule
electron mass m	$= 9{\cdot}1083 \times 10^{-31}$ kg
Planck's constant h	$= 6{\cdot}6252 \times 10^{-34}$ joule sec
rest mass of proton	$= 1{\cdot}6724 \times 10^{-27}$ kg
rest mass of neutron	$= 1{\cdot}6747 \times 10^{-27}$ kg
velocity of light c	$= 2{\cdot}9979 \times 10^{8}$ m/sec

number of molecules
per cubic metre of
ideal gas at s.t.p.
(Loschmidt's number) $N = 2{\cdot}6872 \times 10^{25}$ m^{-3} atm^{-1}

Boltzmann's constant k $= 1{\cdot}3804 \times 10^{-23}$ joule/°K $= 8{\cdot}617 \times 10^{-5}$ eV/°K

electronic charge e	$= 1{\cdot}6021 \times 10^{-19}$ coulomb
(e/m) for electron	$= 1{\cdot}7589 \times 10^{11}$ coul/kg
ε_0	$= 8{\cdot}8542 \times 10^{-12}$ farad/metre

number of molecules
in a gram-molecule
(Avogadro's number) N $= 6{\cdot}0249 \times 10^{23}$

Bohr magneton β	$= 1{\cdot}1653 \times 10^{-29}$ weber/metre
μ_0	$= 4\pi \times 10^{-7}$ henry/metre

Chapter 1

Introduction—The Discovery of the Electron

1.1 Historical background. The aim of this book is to provide a short account of the physics of the electron, as it affects practical applications. We shall be concerned essentially with the developments of the first half of the twentieth century, but these developments can best be understood in relation to the growth of scientific ideas in earlier times.

One of the major scientific achievements of the early nineteenth century was the development of the atomic theory from the intensive study of the laws of chemical combination. The idea of atoms can be traced back to classical Greece, but it was only when the science of chemistry had become quantitative that the atomic theory became relevant to science in anything but a very speculative way. Even before these ideas were consolidated, questions were being raised concerning the nature of the forces between atoms in a chemical compound. Davy had publicized and exploited electrolysis, and suggested that interatomic forces were electrostatic attractions between opposite charges, so for the first time suggesting an intimate connection between matter and electricity.

The work of Faraday elaborated Davy's purely qualitative observations, and established quantitative laws of electrolysis (1833), providing a numerical equivalence between a given quantity of matter decomposed and the quantity of electric charge passing. It follows at once that if matter is to be thought of as atomic in nature, so too must be electricity. The significance of this idea of the atomic nature of electricity was not clearly grasped, but it was never entirely lost. Its real importance remained hidden for many years, until experimental techniques and theoretical ideas had developed sufficiently (and a great deal of development was required) to make use of it.

The appropriate context for this further development was the study of the electrical conductivity of rarified gases; attempts were made to understand this phenomenon in the same way as electrolytic effects. This is the background against which J. J. Thomson's classical experiment (1897) must be seen.

1.2 J. J. Thomson's determination of e/m for cathode rays. During the previous thirty years electrical discharges in gases (at pressures

17

between 1 and 1/100 mmHg) had been studied. The electric current was thought to be carried by an emission from the cathode of the discharge named 'cathode rays'. The nature of the rays was a matter of widespread speculation, but the only tangible idea that was put forward was the suggestion that the rays consisted of charged corpuscles. When it was observed that the rays were deflected by both electric and magnetic fields, it was realized that the ratio of mass to charge of the corpuscles—if corpuscles they were—could be determined. The experiment described was the first to achieve this.

J. J. Thomson's apparatus is shown in Fig. 1.1. The experimental tube was evacuated to a pressure of about 0·01 mmHg and a high voltage discharge was operated between cathode C and anode A in the residual gas in the left-hand chamber. The anode A is a metal diaphragm with a slit 1 mm wide cut in it, which allows a stream of cathode rays to pass through. A collimated beam is obtained by means of a similar slit, aligned with the first, in an earthed diaphragm at the other end of the neck; the beam, now roughly parallel, enters the main chamber. Its subsequent path is inferred from the location of the patch of fluorescence produced where it strikes the end wall of the tube.

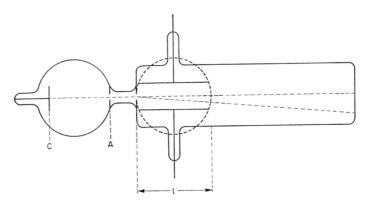

FIG. 1.1   J. J. Thomson's apparatus for the determination of the charge mass ratio of cathode rays.

Where the rays enter the main chamber, they pass between parallel condenser plates of length l. Let us suppose that the rays consist of corpuscles of electric charge e and mass m, moving with a velocity v_x. If an electric field F exists between the plates, then each corpuscle experiences a force eF, acting for a time l/v_x.

The final velocity in the direction of F is

$$v_y = \frac{Fel}{mv_x}.$$

When it leaves the electric field, the particle has been deflected through an angle θ, where

$$\theta = \frac{v_y}{v_x} = \frac{Fel}{mv_x{}^2}.$$

If instead of the electric field, a magnetic field of flux density B perpendicular to the plane of the diagram acts on the particle over the same distance l it will experience a force perpendicular to that field and to its direction of motion. If the deflection is small the force, Bev_x will produce a deflection ϕ, where

$$\phi = \frac{Bel}{mv_x}.$$

In particular, for the case where B is adjusted so that $\theta = \phi$, we can eliminate v_x between these expressions, giving

$$\frac{e}{m} = \frac{F\theta}{B^2l}.$$

The value of e/m found was $1 \cdot 77 \times 10^{11}$ coul/kg.

This is more than 1000 times the value of e/m known for ions in solution, and the result was the same no matter what the residual gas supporting the discharge. These results were taken by Thomson to indicate the presence of a new particle, lighter than the atom, which was later given the name 'electron'.

1.3 **Significance of the experiment.** The very familiarity of this experiment can easily obscure its significance. At present there are two things of particular importance to be said. First, Thomson definitely interpreted his experiment in terms of the deflection of discrete particles. An entirely different interpretation, in terms of the deflection of a continuous stream, as of water from a fire hose, would have been quite feasible and equally effective, but out of keeping with those ideas of the atomic nature of electricity which, as we have seen, were a part of the scientific background of the time. Secondly, the analysis of the results treats the 'atoms' of electricity as if they were like miniature charged pith balls, in that the forces on them in electrostatic or magnetic fields are in accordance with the well-established macroscopic laws.

An extrapolation of known physical laws to cover a scale of events so very different is a bold step. It is therefore one of the really significant features of J. J. Thomson's experiment that it reveals circumstances in which 'cathode rays' do behave *as particles deflected in electric and magnetic fields according to the known laws of electromagnetism,* unaffected by other influences.

1.4 **The scope of electronics.** The science of electronics is essentially a detailed exploration and extension of this statement, and naturally an important part of this process has been to exploit to the full the circumstances of J. J. Thomson's experiment. It may be the *direction* of the electron's motion which is of primary concern, as in the cathode ray tube or the electron microscope. On the other hand, we may be concerned with controlling the *number* of electrons in transit between fixed points, as for instance in the triode. Much of what follows will be concerned with these developments.

1.5 **The interplay of science and technology.** The very wide range of common applications of vacuum electronic devices at the present time brings out another matter of importance, whose operation will be apparent to the reader at many points in the following pages. A careful study of J. J. Thomson's experimental procedure makes clear both the 'string and sealing-wax' technique, and the great difficulty experienced in attaining even a barely adequate vacuum. By contrast, the construction of even the simplest modern valve reveals the application of highly developed special methods of assembly and construction, whilst the manufacture of vacuum pumps and measuring gear of a very high order of performance is in itself a major industry. In this way new technical developments assist the further growth of the science on which they were founded, and this interaction can continue to the mutual benefit of science and technology.

1.6 **Electrons and matter.** The manipulation of electrons in a vacuum which we have been discussing requires that electrons can be introduced into the vacuum. The source of the electrons must be matter in familiar form, and this brings us to another important aspect of Thomson's work, the relation of the electron to bulk matter.

The clue to this relationship was found by Thomson from further experiments. In the work we have described, the electrons originated from an electrical discharge in a gas. Particles of the same e/m were found to be emitted from metals on heating or on irradiation with ultra-violet light. Determination of the electronic charge e confirmed that the large e/m is due to a small mass, and it may be concluded that the electron is a light particle which is a universal constituent of matter. When the electrons are produced in a gas discharge, positive ions are also formed, whose e/m value is of the same order as that for ions in solution, and varies according to the gas used. The idea that the atom has a structure, with the electron as an invariable constituent, is now inescapable; but what sort of structure does the atom have, and how (if at all) does this structure determine its characteristic properties?

This is the theme of much of the physics of the last half-century. We shall summarize it in the next two chapters, and shall then be in a position to see how electrons may be freed in a controlled way for use in vacuum devices.

We shall also begin to see how the knowledge so gained of the behaviour of electrons in gases and solids can be turned to practical account, so that devices can be constructed that are not concerned with electrons in a vacuum. These developments will form the second major topic of this book.

REFERENCES

1. THOMSON, J. J. 'Cathode rays', *Phil. Mag.* **44**, 293 (1897).

2. WHITTAKER, SIR EDMUND. *History of the Theories of the Aether and Electricity*, Revised edn., 2 vols., Nelson, London (1951, 1953).

Chapter 2

Electrons in Atoms

2.1 The inadequacy of classical physics. Given the hypothesis that each atom of matter contains electrons, the way in which they are incorporated in an electrically neutral, stable arrangement must be investigated. J. J. Thomson favoured the idea of electrons distributed in an extended region of diffuse positive charge. It is possible to show that this can lead to a stable arrangement, and it can obviously also be neutral.

The distribution of positive charge was studied experimentally by Rutherford, by investigating the scattering of alpha particles (very energetic doubly ionized helium atoms released in certain types of radioactive disintegration) by the atoms. It was found that the proportion of particles scattered through large angles by an atom was far too big to arise from the repulsion of the alpha particle by a diffuse sphere of positive charge of atomic dimensions. It was necessary to suppose that the alpha particle itself, and the seat of positive charge in the atom, are very small, massive particles (nuclei) with the electrons grouped around them. On this basis a satisfactory theory of the scattering, predicting an angular distribution of alpha particles in good agreement with experiment, is possible. Incidentally, the theory is based on the inverse square law of repulsion between the two nuclei, and its success indicates that the Coulomb law of force is valid for single particles down to distances of 10^{-13} cm.

Now this configuration of electrons around a massive positive nucleus can only be stable if the electrons are in orbital motion relative to the nucleus. Here we encounter a contradiction, for this equilibrium is impossible in terms of our experience of electromagnetism on the large scale. A charged particle subjected to an acceleration must lose energy by electromagnetic radiation; an orbiting electron must be accelerated to constrain it in its orbit, so that it too would be expected to lose energy, which is incompatible with stability. But the stability of most kinds of atoms is a fact of observation of the most inescapable kind, and in this way, consideration of the electron in an atom places us in a dilemma, whose resolution requires a body of ideas completely unfamiliar in the physics of macroscopic bodies.

We must start by focusing attention on something specific, and for this purpose the emission of electromagnetic radiation from an atom will serve very well. The hypothetical nuclear atom considered in the previous paragraph would radiate continuously over a substantial range of wavelengths while its electron orbit would gradually shrink. On the other hand, an actual atom is found to emit radiation only when it is disturbed (excited) by raising it to a high temperature, by passing electric current through a gas or in other ways, and when it does radiate, it emits over such an exceedingly narrow range that we can identify its emission for all practical purposes with a single frequency, giving a spectral 'line' which is characteristic of the particular kind of atom. These lines can occur over a wide range of frequencies from the 'hard' X-ray (wavelength $\sim 10^{-9}$ cm) to the microwave region (wavelength ~ 1 cm). It is quite impossible to reconcile these observations with the classical theory of electromagnetism (developed, it will be noted, by Maxwell in a theoretical analysis implicity based on the continuity, and not the atomicity, of electrical charge).

At this point we are compelled to suppose that the laws of nature developed for macroscopic matter break down for atomic particles. It will be remembered that the experiments of J. J. Thomson indicate that the laws of electromagnetism are at least a very good approximation when describing the motions of free electrons in a vacuum, and also that Rutherford's alpha-particle scattering experiments show that the Coulomb law of force between charges is valid down to distances of 10^{-5} times the radius of the atom. We shall therefore assume provisionally that the laws of electromagnetism are valid, and examine the other features of our extrapolation from the macroscopic to the atomic scale, to see whether any inconsistencies have crept in there.

2.2 **The application of quantum theory.** A valuable clue is provided by the quantum theory of radiation. Both the distribution of the frequencies of electromagnetic radiation emitted by a black body, and the existence of a low-frequency threshold for the photoelectric emission from metals (Section 4.4) are clear-cut phenomena which can be studied by unambiguous experiments, and both are irreconcilable with any explanation related to the classical theory of electromagnetism. Both become intelligible when the process of emission and absorption of radiation is treated in terms of discrete amounts of energy (quanta), which can even be regarded in many respects as particles (photons). The energy of each quantum is proportional to the frequency, in accordance with the relationship adduced by Planck

$$E = h\nu,$$

where E is the energy, ν the frequency, and h is a universal constant (Planck's constant) whose value is $6\cdot6252 \times 10^{-34}$ joule sec. This theory was applied to the simplest atom, the hydrogen atom, by Niels Bohr in 1913, in the following way. Suppose that electrons have *stable* orbits round the nucleus, as common observation suggests they must, and that associated with each orbit is a given quantity of electron energy, kinetic plus potential, say E_1 in the lowest energy or ground state, and E_2 in a state of higher energy which the electron may attain by excitation. The electron may thus change from one stable orbit to another, and in particular may return from the excited to the ground state by the emission of a single quantum of radiation of frequency.

$$hv = E_2 - E_1.$$

As it stands, this is no more than a definite statement of our knowledge— and ignorance— though this is not to deny the revolutionary nature of the formulation. But to the question, how is the motion in the stable orbit to be described, and by what means its energy is to be calculated, there is no hint of an answer at this stage. There took place over the twenty years following Bohr's work an amazing sequence of developments in theoretical physics which provided an answer. The salient features of this development will now be sketched.

2.3   **The role of probability—the uncertainty principle.**   In the first place, if we are to specify the orbit of the electron completely, what must we know? We must know the kind of force field in which the particle moves, and its position and velocity at a chosen instant of time. It may legitimately be assumed that the force field is known—a Coulomb attraction between nucleus and electron. To determine the simultaneous position and velocity (momentum is more usually specified), an experiment must be performed.

It is in the thinking about the sort of experiment which might be carried out, that the special nature of experiments on the atomic scale becomes evident. This is a factor which straightforward extrapolation from the macroscopic scale ignores, and is the reason for the failure of classical theory. Consider, for example, an experiment designed to 'see' the position of an electron. Clearly some sort of microscope is required, but a microscope cannot reveal detail finer than a certain limit—the resolving power— which is limited at best to the order of the wavelength of the light used. Thus visible light could, in principle, reveal the position of the electron to within about 10^{-5} cm, and not with greater precision that that. Clearly, if our concern is to describe stable orbits within the atom, of diameter of the order 10^{-8} cm, this precision is entirely inadequate, and we shall have to consider an instrument making use of electromagnetic waves of much shorter wavelength—for instance, perhaps 10^{-10} cm, in the gamma ray region. Now the microscope will give no information unless the 'light' interacts with the object, but a gamma ray cannot interact with an electron without a considerable amount of energy being exchanged. (From the point of view of the quantum theory the interaction may be seen as the collision of two particles, in which a significant fraction of the photon energy is transferred as 'recoil' to the electron.) This unavoidable change in the energy of the electron in our 'microscope' has the consequence that, in trying to measure the position of the electron in its orbit, we must inevitably alter its momentum. Careful consideration of all possible experiments shows that we can neither measure the position of an electron without modifying the momentum, nor measure the momentum without disturbing the trajectory of the particle. The best hope is a kind of compromise in which related measurements are made such that the disturbance of each is minimized. Instances of the detailed working of this are given in Reference 1 at the end of the chapter.

Hence, no conceivable experiment can provide detailed information of the precise position and momentum of an electron. This was expressed in quantitative form by Heisenberg in 1927. It is known as the *uncertainty principle* and states that the product of the uncertainty in the position of a particle Δq and the corresponding uncertainty of momentum Δp is given by
$$\Delta p.\Delta q \gtrsim h.$$
Since no experiment can determine p and q precisely at the same instant of time, we can no longer hope ever to determine exactly the orbit of an electron in an atom—the attempt to do so will excite the electron into a different orbit. Since science must concern itself with quantities which are experimentally observable, it is not surprising that we were led to contradiction when we sought to predict an orbit which is not experimentally observable—we asked a foolish question, and have no right to be surprised at receiving a foolish answer.

Since our experimental information about an electron orbit cannot be free from some uncertainty, we must build the limitation into our theory by making it *statistical*, i.e. by looking for the *probability* that an electron will at a given time have position q and momentum p. This is the first stage towards an understanding of the state of an electron in an atom. We must now pass on to consider how to formulate a theory in terms of probabilities. The study of a suitable theory is the concern of *quantum mechanics*.

2.4 **Electromagnetic radiation—a comparison.** Consider for a moment the situation with regard not to matter but to electromagnetic radiation. In classical electromagnetism we are usually concerned with vectors **E** and **H** but what really concerns us—what we measure—is energy, and it would be more satisfactory, from some viewpoints at least, to think habitually in terms of the Poynting vector
$$\mathbf{N} = \mathbf{E} \wedge \mathbf{H},$$

describing energy flux, or in terms of the energy density

$$\tfrac{1}{2} \left(\varepsilon_0 \, E^2 + \mu_0 \, H^2 \right).$$

Of course we still have to know our $\mathbf{E}$'s and $\mathbf{H}$'s throughout, and to keep track of them through the algebra while retaining the essential separateness of each, we could work with a single complex variable

$$\mathbf{P} = \mathbf{E} + i\mathbf{H}$$

instead of working with the separate real functions $\mathbf{E}$ and $\mathbf{H}$, although this is never done in electromagnetism, such is the force of tradition.

Now, how do these things relate to the quantum theory of radiation? If radiation is only available in quantized packets $E = h\nu$, the energy density divided by $h\nu$ is equal to the photon density. Another way of expressing the same thing is in terms of the probability of finding a photon at a given place at a given time—that is to say, a statistical interpretation. Any mathematical result in electromagnetic theory, or in physical optics (which amounts to the same thing), could be expressed in terms of our single complex variable $\mathbf{P}$ and interpreted statistically, in terms of the probability of finding a photon at a given point. The key to all problems of this sort would then be Maxwell's equations, expressed in terms of the new variable $\mathbf{P}$.

Thus, although there is only a single mathematical theory of radiation, its interpretation has two aspects, wave and particle, and the observed behaviour in particular circumstances is likely to emphasize one or the other. Thus, interference experiments stress the wave properties, whereas photoelectricity stresses the particle properties.

2.5   **The wave aspect of matter.**   At first sight, any attempt to develop analogies between our problem of electrons in atoms and this treatment of radiation would seem far-fetched in the extreme. Yet, in treating radiation, we have been forced to recognize that it has particle-like aspects—is our belief in underlying symmetries in nature strong enough to take us further? An act of faith of this type was made in 1924 by Louis de Broglie, similar to the one we are contemplating, but based on the literal interpretation of certain mathematical symmetries in the theory of relativity. De Broglie introduced the idea of matter waves associated with a particle, whose wavelength λ is related to the momentum p of the particle by the relationship $\lambda = h/p$.

The matter waves were first mooted in de Broglie's doctoral thesis. His examiners were disturbed by the largely speculative nature of the idea, and sought the advice of Einstein, who was able to reassure them of the importance of the new development.

Very shortly afterwards, the new idea was confirmed by experimental results from an unexpected quarter. Davisson and Germer, investigating the secondary emission (Section 4.18) of metal single crystals, found that the electron beam was reflected strongly from the crystal in certain directions, in a way closely comparable with the diffraction of X-rays. In the latter case the regular array of scattering atoms in the crystal acts as a three-dimensional diffraction grating. By analogy with the X-rays a 'wavelength' could be calculated for the electrons, knowing the spacing of the atoms in the crystal, and this wavelength was found to depend on the electron momentum in accordance with the de Broglie relation.

Diffraction phenomena are of great value in determining the arrangement and spacing of atoms in a crystal. The diffraction of X-rays is widely used for this purpose, but under special circumstances electron diffraction can be of more value. In addition, we can have recourse to the diffraction of slow neutrons from a reactor (whose de Broglie wavelength is also of the order of the interatomic distance in crystals) and sometimes this technique is more informative than X-ray methods of crystal measurement. The accumulated results of these studies constitute formidable experimental evidence for the existence of de Broglie waves.

In other words, circumstances have been discovered which reveal the wave-like properties of matter, as opposed to the particle-like properties which have previously monopolized attention. Different circumstances emphasize one mode of behaviour or the other, just as in the case of radiation (Section 2.4).

2.6 The Schrödinger wave equation.

Now it should be possible to express the theory of de Broglie waves in terms of differential equations, as in the case of electromagnetic waves (Maxwell's equations). We can look for a differential equation in terms of a variable ψ such that, by analogy with the energy density in electromagnetic theory, ψ is a complex variable

$$\psi(xyz) = f + ig,$$

and

$$f^2 + g^2 = \psi\psi^*$$

is the probability of finding a particle at the point (x, y, z). Note that ψ^* is the complex conjugate of ψ.

The *wave function* ψ for a particle must be defined in terms of the particle energy (kinetic plus potential), and the force field in which it is situated, best described through the potential energy V. The differential equation for ψ is

$$\frac{\partial^2\psi}{\partial x^2} + \frac{\partial^2\psi}{\partial y^2} + \frac{\partial^2\psi}{\partial z^2} + \frac{2m}{\hbar^2}(E-V)\psi = 0,$$

where E is the total, V the potential energy, m is the mass of the particle, and $\hbar$ is used to denote $h/2\pi$. This was first given in 1925 by E. Schrödinger, and is referred to as the *Schrödinger wave equation*, or sometimes just the *wave equation*. The equation cannot be proved in any general or satisfying way. It is a prescription for calculating electron energies and probability distributions in space, and which provides therefore the very information that we can hope to obtain experimentally for an electron system. It stands or falls by the agreement or otherwise of theoretical predictions with experimental findings; such agreement, to date, has been substantial and extensive, limited only by the difficulty of solving the equation for physically interesting—or indeed realizable—conditions. An important branch of quantum mechanics concerns itself with the mathematical problems which are encountered in the attempt. In fact the Schrödinger equation has served physics very well, and some aspects of its usefulness will be apparent in this book.

Note that the equation as quoted above does not include time—it is in fact a restricted form of a more general Schrödinger equation. This is because we shall only be concerned with steady or 'stationary' states. This still affords considerable scope, just as it would be possible to cover a lot of interesting ground in electromagnetism by considering only 'standing wave' patterns.

The simplest case of an electron in an atom is the hydrogen atom, consisting of a single electron moving in the field of a nucleus of equal positive charge. Even in this case the solution of the Schrödinger equation is quite lengthy and involved, and it will be omitted here for the sake of brevity. We do need to consider the form of the solutions, and to get a feeling for their nature, but it will suffice to consider instead a simpler example of a wave equation. All equations describing periodic phenomena have common features, and we shall consider one of the simplest possible, namely the one-dimensional problem of the propagation of transverse waves in a stretched string.

2.7　Transverse vibrations in strings.

Let the ends of the string be defined by $x = 0$, $x = l$, then if y is the transverse deflection, and t is time, the general wave equation will be reduced to one dimension, and have the form

$$\frac{\partial^2 y}{\partial x^2} = \frac{1}{c^2}\frac{\partial^2 y}{\partial t^2},$$

where c is the wave velocity. The boundary conditions are $y = 0$ at $x = 0$, $x = l$, and must be satisfied at all times. We must therefore try a solution in which the variables are separable.

$$y = X(x)\,T(t);$$

this gives

$$\frac{1}{X}\frac{d^2X}{dx^2} = \frac{1}{c^2T}\frac{d^2T}{dt^2}.$$

The terms are identically equal, yet independent, and must be constant. Write this as $-p^2$; then, for the L.H.S.

$$\frac{d^2X}{dx^2} + p^2X = 0.$$

$X = \cos px$ or $X = \sin px$ are solutions, but only the latter satisfies the boundary conditions at $x = 0$.

To satisfy also the condition at $x = l$, we must have

$$\sin pl = 0, \text{ or } pl = n\pi,$$

where n is an integer, whence $p = \dfrac{n\pi}{l}$.

Taking now the R.H.S. of the equation

$$\frac{d^2T}{dt^2} + c^2p^2T = 0,$$

$$T = a\cos\frac{n\pi ct}{l} + b\sin\frac{n\pi ct}{l}$$

is a solution (substituting for p). Combining the solutions:

$$y = \sin\frac{n\pi x}{l}\left(a\cos\frac{n\pi ct}{l} + b\sin\frac{n\pi ct}{l}\right),$$

which may be written as

$$y = A\sin\frac{n\pi x}{l}\cos\left[\frac{n\pi ct}{l} + \varepsilon\right].$$

the value of n defines the *harmonic* of the string. Any arbitrary disturbance can be expressed as a sum of the harmonics.

It is possible to go on from this result to calculate the potential and kinetic energies of the vibrating string. The *total* energy is

$$\frac{\pi^2c^2p^2A^2n^2}{4l}$$

when $\rho = $ mass/length, and $c = $ velocity of propagation of waves. Note: energy is proportional to n^2.

For a similar problem in two dimensions, for instance a vibrating plate, we will have *two* separate integers analogous to n, to specify the harmonics.

In a similar way, if a solution of the Schrödinger equation is to be possible, certain conditions must be satisfied by the energy, and these conditions involve integral numbers, called in this case *quantum numbers*.

2.8 The solution of the Schrödinger equation for the hydrogen atom.

We will now examine the solution of the Schrödinger equation for the hydrogen atom, which, if expressed in spherical polar co-ordinates, can be separated as follows:

$$\psi \, (r\theta\phi) = R_{nl} \, (r) \, \Theta_{lm} \, (\theta) \, \Phi_m \, (\phi),$$

where $\Phi_m \, (\phi) = \dfrac{1}{\sqrt{2\pi}} \exp \, (im\phi),$

$$\Theta_{lm} \, (\theta) = - \left[\frac{(2l+1) \, (l-|m|)!}{2(l+|m|) \, !} \right]^{\frac{1}{2}} P_l^{|m|} \cos \theta,$$

and

$$R_{nl}(r) = - \left[\left(\frac{2}{na_0} \right)^3 \frac{(n-l-1)!}{2n \, \{(n+l)!\}^3} \right]^{\frac{1}{2}} \left[\exp \left(-\frac{\rho}{2} \right) \right] \left[\rho^l \, L_{n+1}^{2l+1}(\rho) \right].$$

In these expressions P and L are polynominals which need not concern us,

$$\rho = \frac{2}{na_0} \, r, \text{ and } a_0 = \frac{h^2}{4\pi^2 m_e^2},$$

where m_e is the electron mass

Notice that there are three quantum numbers, n, l, m, but they are not independent; in fact

$$|m| \leqslant l < n.$$

Although they appear as mere ciphers in the solution of a mathematical problem, the quantum numbers do have a physical significance:

(i) The value of n is equal to the number of nodes (points of zero value) of the radial wave function as r increases. Between successive nodes there are maxima of probability density which represent electron 'orbits' as closely as we can hope to define them. Hence n indicates the maximum number of orbits associated with the given state.

(ii) The quantum number l represents the total orbital angular momentum of the electron in the given state. The angular momentum is quantized, and restricted to the values

$$\hbar \sqrt{l(l+1)}.$$

(iii) If we chose an axis in space, then the component of orbital angular momentum along this axis is also quantized. The maximum values possible are $\pm l\hbar$ (the signs refer to opposite directions) and we can also have $\pm (l-1)\hbar, \pm (l-2)\hbar \ldots 0$, because $|m| \leqslant l$, $m\hbar$ represents the value of this component.

2.9 **Spin.** The great value of the Schrödinger equation, as a keystone of electron theory, has been made plain already. If it is to justify this exalted role, it must be expected to meet the requirements of the theory of relativity, and remain unchanged for any observer moving with any uniform velocity with respect to the particle to which it is being applied. The other generalizations of theoretical physics (for instance Maxwell's equations) satisfy this requirement, but unfortunately the Schrödinger equation as we have formulated it does not. In 1928 P. M. Dirac was able to show that the equation could be made to satisfy this criterion, i.e. 'relativistically invariant'. For our purposes, there is no need to complicate matters by writing down a modified form of the equation, for we shall not be concerned with high energy conditions for which the effects of relativity are of themselves significant. Instead it is sufficient to keep the same form of the equation, but to remember that we must specifiy an extra quantum number, s, which is restricted to the two values $\frac{1}{2}$ and $-\frac{1}{2}$. With this addition the requirement of relativistic invariance is met. Like the other quantum numbers, s has its physical significance, for if we regard the electron as a charged sphere of finite though small size, it will have angular momentum due to spin about its own axis, and if this quantity is calculated it is found to be

$$\hbar \sqrt{s(s+\tfrac{1}{2})},$$

so that s is referred to as the *spin quantum number*.

2.10 **Energy levels for hydrogen.** The energy of a stationary state in the hydrogen atom is principally determined by n. The relationship is

$$E_n = -\frac{2\pi^2 m_e e^4}{h^2 n^2}.$$

All the quantities on the right-hand side are known, so we can calculate the energies for a given n. A convenient unit of energy for use in discussing electron energies in atoms is the energy acquired by an electron in falling through a potential difference of one volt—the *electronvolt* (eV).

$$1 \text{ electronvolt} = 1 \cdot 602 \times 10^{-19} \text{ joule.}$$

The calculated energies for the hydrogen atom are given in Fig. 2.1 in electronvolts for the values of n shown, each n value labelling an energy level. Now, according to the Bohr theory (Section 2.2) for the origin of spectra, transitions between different levels should take place with the emission—or absorption—of a quantum of frequency

$$h\nu = E_2 - E_1.$$

Some possible transitions of this sort are shown on the diagram. All the transitions shown correspond to lines in the observed hydrogen spectrum,

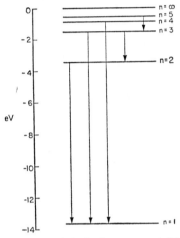

FIG. 2.1   Some energy levels of the hydrogen atom. The lowest state shown is the ground state, the highest the ionization level. The arrows indicate some of the possible transitions, corresponding to a line spectrum.

and their frequencies are accurately predicted. This is one, among many, of the impressive triumphs of the Schrödinger equation.

It will be noticed from Fig. 2.1 that the energy levels crowd together as the principal quantum number is increased, converging to a limit of zero (the energy scale we use is negative). The zero refers to the potential energy of an electron at infinite distance, that is to say an electron freed from the atom altogether, or ionized. The energy difference between this zero and the atomic state of lowest energy (the *ground state*) is the energy that must be supplied to the atom to ionize the electron and, expressed in (electron) volts, is known as the *ionization potential*.

2.11   Complex atoms—general principles.   What of the more complex atoms? The hydrogen nucleus is reckoned a fundamental particle (the proton) and it has a positive charge equal in magnitude to the electronic charge. All other nuclei are compounds of protons and neutrons, the neutron having a mass almost identical with that of the proton, but no charge. The forces which bind the constituent particles in the nucleus must be very strong to give the nucleus its stability in the normal terrestrial environment (Section 8.6) but their nature is not clearly understood. It can at least be said that the known atomic nuclei represent stable aggregations of the particles (except for radioactive nuclei which are of course unstable).

For electrical neutrality, the number of electrons in the *atom* must equal the number of protons in the *nucleus*. It is the number of electrons which serves to distinguish an atomic species chemically, so that each chemical element has a nucleus with a different charge. (Nuclei with the same number of protons combined with different numbers of neutrons are *isotopes*. For instance there are three isotopes of hydrogen, whose nuclei contain respectively a single proton, a proton plus a neutron (deuterium) and a proton plus two neutrons (tritium).)

Where the number of electrons in the atom exceeds one, the energy of the atom as a whole will involve the mutual interactions of the electrons. A rigorous attack on this problem is generally quite impossible, but an acceptable approximation is to solve the problem of finding the energy levels of one particular electron in a spherically symmetric field composed of that of the nucleus, modified by a 'smeared out' average of the effect of the other electrons which we regard as partially screening our chosen electron from the nuclear field. This modification of the field only affects the numerical values of the solution of the Schrödinger equation, and not its form, so possible stationary states will still be represented by the same quantum numbers, and hence the solution of the hydrogen atom problem is more important than it appears, because it provides a framework for dealing with *all* atoms.

2.12 Complex atoms—the building process and the Pauli principle.

It is possible, when dealing with atoms containing more than one electron, to imagine the nucleus 'stripped' of all electrons and the electrons being added one at a time. In this way we can determine the states (as labelled by quantum numbers) occupied by the different electrons. It might be thought that all the electrons would congregate in that state having the lowest energy, but this is not so. In fact a rule—the *Pauli exclusion principle*—has been enunciated to cover the allocation of the electrons; it states that *no two electrons can be represented by the same wave function and have identical values for all the quantum numbers.* This applies, not only to the problem of electrons in atoms, but to any configura-

c

tion. We shall see its importance when discussing electrons in crystals in Chapter 9.

We can at once apply the exclusion principle to the arrangement of electrons in atoms of increasing atomic number, for since the wave functions of the electron states are the same, the quantum numbers must have the following values. Starting with hydrogen:

$$1 \text{ electron:} \qquad n = 1, \quad l = 0 \quad (s = +\tfrac{1}{2} \text{ or } -\tfrac{1}{2})$$

then helium

$$2 \text{ electrons:} \qquad \begin{aligned} n &= 1, \quad l = 0 \quad (s = +\tfrac{1}{2}) \\ n &= 1, \quad l = 0 \quad (s = -\tfrac{1}{2}) \end{aligned}$$

lithium

$$3 \text{ electrons:} \quad \begin{aligned} &2 \text{ with } n = 1, \quad l = 0 \quad (s = \pm\tfrac{1}{2}) \\ &1 \text{ with } n = 2, \quad l = 0 \end{aligned}$$

beryllium

$$4 \text{ electrons:} \quad \begin{aligned} &2 \text{ with } n = 1, \quad l = 0 \\ &2 \text{ with } n = 2, \quad l = 0 \end{aligned}$$

boron

$$5 \text{ electrons:} \quad \begin{aligned} &2 \text{ with } n = 1, \quad l = 0 \\ &2 \text{ with } n = 2, \quad l = 0 \\ &1 \text{ with } n = 2, \quad l = 1 \end{aligned}$$

carbon

$$6 \text{ electrons:} \quad \begin{aligned} &2 \text{ with } n = 1, \quad l = 0 \\ &2 \text{ with } n = 2, \quad l = 0 \\ &2 \text{ with } n = 2, \quad l = 1 \end{aligned}$$

nitrogen

$$7 \text{ electrons:} \quad \begin{aligned} &2 \text{ with } n = 1, \quad l = 0 \\ &2 \text{ with } n = 2, \quad l = 0 \\ &3 \text{ with } n = 2, \quad l = 1 \end{aligned}$$

and so on.

All possible quantum states for a given value of n are referred to collectively as a *shell*. With neon, the shell with $n = 2$ has been filled, and further electrons must occupy states with $n = 3$, where the addition of eight electrons will bring us to the argon configuration. There is thus a cyclical element in the electronic 'architecture' of the atoms which is a complete parallel to the Mendeléeff periodic classification of the elements.

This classification was itself derived on the basis of purely chemical evidence, and the fact that it corresponds to the periodicity of the energy levels occupied by the electrons, is experimental evidence for the Schrödinger equation, which because the whole of chemistry is brought to bear on the issue, is in its way more remarkable than the agreement with the hydrogen spectra. A useful form of the periodic table is to be found at the end of this book.

For values of the principal quantum number greater than 2, there is a greater number of permitted states, 18 in fact for $n = 3$ and 32 for $n = 4$. This can be verified by the reader, with reference to the permitted values of l, m, s for given n. The importance of this is far-reaching and must now be considered.

2.13 **Energy levels of complex atoms.** A question which we have so far neglected to ask now demands attention: in what order are the states with given n filled as the electrons are added, in imagination, one by one? Those states with lowest energy will be filled first, but we have regarded the energy as determined by the value of the principal quantum number alone. For an atom containing many electrons, this is incorrect, for although n determines the size of the orbit, its shape (ellipticity) is determined by the l-value, so an eccentric orbit of given area will pass much more closely to the nucleus than a spherical or nearly spherical one of the same area. Regarding the effect of the other electrons as averaged into a screening field, the influence of this field—and hence the electron energy—depends on the ellipticity of the orbit, and hence on l.

When this effect is taken into account it is found that the smaller l-values have the smaller energy, and the extent of this effect is sufficiently large to make the energy of states with $n = 4$, $l = 0$ less than that of $n = 3$, $l = 2$, so that, at this stage in atom-building, electrons enter the 'outer' shell, and it is only when the second $n = 4$, $l = 0$ electron has been added that the vacant levels are filled. This and similar interruptions in the smooth process of electron addition gives rise to the 'transition metals' in the periodic table.

A more extreme case of the same type occurs with $n = 4$, $l = 3$ which only fill when not only the lower states of the $n = 5$ shell but also $n = 6$, $l = 0$ are occupied. Their filling then gives rise to the *rare earth* elements.

This point is of more than academic interest to us in this book, for all these atoms contain incomplete inner shells, and, unlike a complete or closed shell, will have a resultant angular momentum, and an associated magnetic moment. It is for that reason that almost all materials whose magnetic properties are of any practical interest contain transition or rare earth atoms or ions.

To summarize, we have seen how the classical theory of the interaction between electrons and positive ions in atoms has to be replaced by something more adequate, and how the Schrödinger equation provides the necessary basis. It can be used to calculate accurately the energies of electron states in the hydrogen atom, and to provide us with the means of classifying the electron levels in more complex atoms. To *calculate* the energy levels for these latter is generally impossible, and our knowledge of them is based on the results of spectroscopic determinations. The spectra of most atoms are exceedingly complex, and only with the guidance of theory are we able to use this data to derive a knowledge of the energy levels of an atom.

References

1. HEISENBERG, W. C. *Physical Principles of Quantum Theory* (trans. G. Eckart and F. C. Hoyt), University of Chicago Press, Chicago (1930).

2. HEITLER, W. *Elementary Wave Mechanics with Applications to Quantum Chemistry*, 2nd edn., Oxford University Press, Oxford (1956).

3. HUME-ROTHERY, W. *Atomic Theory for Students of Metallurgy*, 2nd edn., Institute of Metals, London (1952).

Problems

2.1 Find the quantum energy (in eV) of:
   (a) A gamma ray of wavelength 1×10^{-12}m
   (b) Green light of wavelength 5461 Å (1 Å $= 10^{-10}$m)
   (c) 3 cm microwaves.
   If the source of each of the above is 1/100 watt, how many quanta are emitted per second in each case?

2.2 Prove that the momentum of a photon of energy E is E/c, and show that a photon cannot give up all its energy on collision with a free electron. (Hint: Momentum as well as energy must be conserved in the transaction.)

2.3 How closely can the velocity of an electron be specified when the electron is confined to a volume of: 1 cm^3; 10^{-24} cm^3; 10^{-39} cm^3? Express the results also in terms of kinetic energy, in eV.

2.4   What is the de Broglie wavelength of the following:

10 V electrons

1000 V electrons

1 MeV (10^6eV) protons (H$^+$)

'Thermal' neutrons, i.e. neutrons with a kinetic energy of 1/40 eV.

Rifle bullets, mass 1.1 gm, velocity 300 m/sec

2.5   Prove that the energy E of an electron (mass m, charge e) in a circular orbit round a nucleus of charge Ze is

$$E = \frac{2\pi^2 m Z^2 e^4}{h^2 n^2}$$

where n is an integer. The following assumptions may be made:

(i) The force between the electron and the nucleus is a Coulomb force.

(ii) The nucleus is sufficiently massive compared with the electron to be considered at rest.

(iii) Those orbits are stable for which the angular momentum of the electron is an integral multiple of $h/2\pi$.

2.6   The hydrogen spectrum in the visible region consists of discrete lines of the following wavelengths: (in Å) 6562·79; 4861·33; 4340·47; 4101·74; 3970·07; 3889·05; 3797·90

Show that their *frequencies* can be fitted by a formula of the type

$$\nu = R \left(1/n_1^2 - 1/n_2^2\right)$$

where $n_1 = 2$, and n_2 has a different integral value for each line.

By relating the expression to the difference of two energy terms of the type given in Question 2.5:

(i) Use the given data to find the value of the electronic charge,

(ii) Find the ionization potential of hydrogen,

(iii) Calculate the radius of the smallest stable orbit.

(iv) Helium which has lost one electron (He$^+$) has the same electronic configuration as hydrogen. What wavelengths in the spectrum of He$^+$ correspond to the given hydrogen lines?

Chapter 3

Forces between Atoms

3.1 **Introduction.** Our major concern with the atom is its influence on the properties of matter in bulk. The simplest situation is the gas, where the molecules move independently, and interact only by collision. Before enlarging on this the main presupposition of the kinetic theory of gases, we must emphasize the distinction between the atom and the molecule, a distinction which took nineteenth century chemistry many decades to elucidate. The atom is the smallest unit of chemical individuality, but the free atom is a rarity and the smallest freely-occurring unit—the molecule— usually contains two or more atoms. With the contents of the previous chapter fresh in mind, it is better to discuss the mechanism of atomic aggregation before considering the collective behaviour of molecules in a gas. This approach is even more important in relation to the behaviour of solids, where the atoms are in no sense independent and interatomic forces are all-important.

3.2 **Molecules.** An understanding of free atoms is clearly necessary for any understanding of the behaviour of matter; but it is equally certain that for most problems, this knowledge is insufficient. Free atoms are rarely encountered under ordinary circumstances since only the inert gases are monatomic at room temperature. The common property that gives these elements their name suggests that in these atoms we encounter an electron configuration which is really stable. Its characteristic feature, as we saw in Section 2.11, is a filled outer shell of electrons. Experience shows that free atoms of other kinds can usually achieve a more stable arrangement by the grouping of the atoms into polyatomic molecules.

In these circumstances, a study of the energies of electrons in molecules is important and indeed unavoidable. We have already seen that the problem of finding the energy states of a single atom containing many electrons is intractable enough. A molecule, having at least two nuclei, cannot offer even the initial simplification of a spherically symmetric field. Nevertheless, considerable progress has been made, through skilful use of approximations. We will illustrate the results first with reference to the hydrogen molecule, the simplest possible diatomic unit.

3.3 **The hydrogen molecule.** Consider first two hydrogen atoms, so far apart that mutual interaction is quite negligible. The situation is shown, for the ground state electronic levels, in Fig. 3.1. If now we imagine the atoms to approach each other, interaction will gradually become more and more significant, and its effect is to split the levels into two, one above and one below the position of the free atom levels, the separation depending on the distance apart. The electrons contributed by

FIG. 3.1 The outermost pair of lines represents the ground state electronic level of two hydrogen atoms at infinite separation. When the atoms approach the levels are split into two, as shown by the arrows, tending to the levels of the hydrogen molecule shown at the centre.

each atom can both occupy the lower level provided the spins are opposed, so that the total electron energy of the new arrangement will be less than that of each atom separately. The two nuclei will take up an equilibrium separation where the reduction in electronic energy arising from a further decrease in interatomic distance is just compensated by the increase of energy arising from the repulsion of the nuclei. This will be the internuclear distance characteristic of the hydrogen molecule. It is hence clear that if two hydrogen atoms collide, they are likely to coalesce, provided that they can get rid of the energy of $2 \cdot 17$ eV ($50 \cdot 4$ kcal per mole) 'saved' by combination. The figure in brackets is the *molar heat of reaction* for the chemical change

$$H + H \rightarrow H_2$$

We can regard the energetics of combination of two atoms of different species in an entirely similar way.

3.4 **Exchange energy.** The forces which bind hydrogen atoms in the molecule are purely electrostatic, and the molecule represents the most favourable configuration of the electron 'charge cloud' (corresponding to the spreading out of the electrons according to the value of $\psi\psi^*$, to give a time average of their position), with respect to the two nuclei. The shape of charge cloud that is attained will depend on the electron states available and hence on the Pauli exclusion principle, so that the reduction of the electron energy in the molecule can be related to the spin states of the electrons and is sometimes called the *exchange energy*. The emphasis on the spin is of importance when considering ferromagnetism (Section 12.12), but otherwise it makes the exchange energy seem rather mysterious, and for that reason we wish to stress its electrostatic origin.

3.5   **The instability of the helium 'molecule'.**   Let us consider now the case of two atoms of helium, initially far apart, and gradually brought closer. The energy levels are similar to those for hydrogen, and there will again be splitting, but there are now four electrons to be distributed, so that both components of the split level will be occupied. Because of the asymmetry of the splitting (Fig. 3.1) the energy of the 'molecule' will in this case be greater than that of the two atoms separately, and there will be no tendency for coalescence on collision.

3.6   **The covalent bond.**   Returning to the hydrogen molecule, we can regard the pair of electrons with opposed spins in the lower level as themselves possessing the characteristic stability of the whole arrangement —regarding them, in fact, as a 'bond' consisting of electrons shared between the two atoms. The 'bond' idea was, of course, already firmly established in chemistry as an empirical picture giving specific meaning to the accumulated experience on the scope of chemical change. We can now be more specific and describe this kind of bond as a *covalent* or *electron-pair* bond.

Covalent bonding can also occur when there is more than one electron in a subshell. For instance there is the important example of the carbon atom, with four electrons of principal quantum number 2. Each of the electrons can form a covalent bond with a hydrogen atom, to produce a molecule of methane, CH_4; or with an atom of chlorine to form a molecule of carbon tetrachloride. The heats of reaction are $20 \cdot 3$ and $21 \cdot 6$ kcal/mole respectively, showing the stability of the molecules with respect to their constituent atoms. The 'electron charge cloud' of the carbon atom is not spherically symmetrical, and there are in fact four symmetrical 'lobes', one for each electron, so that the molecules of CH_4 and CCl_4 are tetrahedral. The fact that the covalent bonds have a specific direction is important.

Like hydrogen, atoms of carbon can combine with themselves, but because we have four bonds per atom, we can build up a carbon 'molecule' which is in this case an endless structure, a regular network in which each atom has four near neighbours. The regularity is characteristic of a crystal, and the structure is in fact that of diamond. The strength of the bonds gives diamond its hardness and inertness.

Other elements from Group IV of the periodic table can form four covalent bonds in a similar way, and crystals of silicon and germanium have the same structure as diamond. We shall discuss their significance as semiconductors in Chapter 10.

3.7   **The ionic bond.**   The ability to form covalent bonds is best developed in those atoms, like carbon, where an electron shell is half-full or nearly so. In the case of an atom with only a single electron in the outer shell, for instance sodium, compound formation is more likely to take place by the transfer of the electron to another atom 'electronegative' enough to receive it—as, for instance, chlorine. This electron transfer will complete the outer shell of the chlorine atom and we shall be left with two ions, of opposite charge, both having the stable inert gas structure and bound together by Coulomb attraction. This is described as an *ionic* bond. Unlike the covalent bond it has no specific direction, and in the rock salt crystal the arrangement of the ions is simply the one which will surround each negative ion as closely as possible with positive ions, and vice versa. In similar ionic compounds, as for instance caesium chloride, the structure of the crystal is different, but simply because in this case the two ions differ considerably in size so that a different form of packing will give a lower potential energy. In a liquid of high permittivity, like water, the interionic binding will be much reduced and the ions will disperse to give an electrolyte solution.

Ionic and covalent bonding represent extreme ways in which electron redistribution will accompany chemical change. In most cases the bonding will be of an intermediate character—we might call it unequal sharing—but the discussion given provides an adequate qualitative picture of the electronic aspects of chemical change.

3.8 **The kinetic theory of gases.** We have considered examples where atoms combine to form stable molecules, like H_2 and CH_4. The gaseous state of matter is characterized by the independence of the molecules. The kinetic theory of gases seeks to explain the properties of a gas in terms of the random motion of the molecules, which interact with each other only by elastic collisions. Implicit in this theory is a picture of the molecule as a miniature, perfectly elastic sphere, a picture which does not accord very well with what we have said about molecular structure. In spite of this the kinetic theory has been very successful, and its deliberate simplicity is not to be despised. Progress has been made with many of the topics discussed in this book simply because it has been possible to use a very simple model, provided only that it is not inconsistent with quantum mechanics, which none the less is kept very much in the background. The kinetic theory is no exception, and we shall find many of its results useful in what follows. A few of the more important will be summarized here.

Let us suppose that unit volume of our model gas contains n molecules, of mass m, average velocity $\bar{v}$ and root-mean-square velocity $\sqrt{(\bar{v^2})}$. (Since the molecular motion is random it would be unreasonable to suppose that all the molecules had a constant velocity, but we propose to avoid the inessential complexities arising from the distribution of velocities, and shall use instead appropriate averages.)

Consider first the most fundamental measurable property of a gas—its pressure. This will arise from momentum transfer from the electrons to the walls of the containing vessel. The reader will be able to verify for himself the relation

$$P = \tfrac{1}{3}\, nm\overline{v^2}.$$

From the equation of state for the gas for unit volume, we have $P = nkT$, where k is Boltzmann's constant and T the absolute temperature, so

$$\tfrac{3}{2}kT = \tfrac{1}{2}\, m\overline{v^2}.$$

The expression on the right-hand side is the average kinetic energy of the gas molecules, which is hence directly related to the temperature of the gas. At room temperature this energy is about $\tfrac{1}{40}$ eV.

3.9 Collisions between molecules—mean free path and cross section.

As a next step, we are interested in the collisions of molecules not only with the walls, but with each other. We now need to consider the area of cross section of the molecule, which we shall assume to be a sphere of diameter d. Taking one particular molecule, it will collide with any other whose centre lies within a cylinder of diameter $2d$ swept out by the first molecule in the course of its motion.

The volume of this cylinder swept out per second is $\pi\, d^2\, \overline{v}$, where $\overline{v}$ is the mean (not r.m.s.) velocity. This volume contains $\pi d^2 \overline{v} n$ molecules, and this will be equal to the number of collisions per second. This quantity is proportional to the *probability* of a collision occurring. Finally, the average distance between collisions, the *mean free path*, is

$$\lambda = 1/\pi d^2 n.$$

A more accurate calculation would allow for movement of molecules into, and out of, the cylindrical volume, and this introduces a factor of $1/\sqrt{2}$. Finally, we can generalize the result for an alien molecule of diameter d_1 moving in a gas of molecular radius d_2:

$$\lambda = \frac{4}{\sqrt{2\,[\pi(d_1 + d_2)^2 n]}}.$$

It is clear that the mean free path, and the probability of collision, must depend on the size of the molecule concerned. In dealing with real molecules, which are rarely anything like spherical, we can retain the same ideas, and discuss the collision probability in terms of an *effective cross section*. This is particularly valuable when we are thinking of more complex phenomena than elastic collisions. Suppose, for instance, that we shoot particles of high energy into a gas, where the particle energy is sufficient to ionize the gas. The probability of it doing so can be expressed in terms of a cross section for ionization (Chapter 7).

It is important to note that since the mean free path is inversely proportional to n the number density of molecules it is therefore inversely proportional to pressure. Thus for example the mean free path of neon at s.t.p. is $1 \cdot 93 \times 10^{-3}$ cm, but it is $1 \cdot 15 \times 10^{-2}$ cm at 1 mmHg pressure. The mean free paths of other gas molecules are generally within a factor of two or three of this value.

3.10 **Transport processes.** We are now led to a simple-minded view of *transport phenomena*, in which the gas is no longer in equilibrium, and energy transfer is taking place. We shall discuss the simple case of a density gradient in one dimension, when the energy transfer takes the form of a migration of molecules (diffusion). Consider a region of density gradient, and take a reference plane in it, normal to the gradient. On average, atoms reaching it from the left will have come from a plane distance λ, the mean free path from the reference plane. The number arriving per second will be

$$\tfrac{1}{6} c \left(n - \lambda \frac{dn}{dx} \right),$$

(since on average one-sixth of the population of molecules will be travelling in a given direction).

The number reaching the reference plane from the right will be

$$\tfrac{1}{6} c \left(n + \lambda \frac{dn}{dx} \right),$$

so that the net rate of flow of molecules across the plane is

$$- \tfrac{1}{3} c\lambda \frac{dn}{dx} = \frac{dn}{dt}.$$

By comparison with the law of diffusion

$$\frac{dn}{dt} = - D \frac{dn}{dx},$$

where D is the diffusion constant, whose value is hence:

$$D = \tfrac{1}{3} c\lambda.$$

3.11 **The Boltzmann distribution.** We have introduced average velocities $\bar{v}$ and $\overline{v^2}$ which we have used as required. Since the motion of the molecules is random, the instantaneous velocities of the molecules will clearly cover a wide range of values. We shall avoid all the (to us) inessential complications arising from the consideration of these velocity distributions in detail, but there is one feature which is important. Supposing a possible energy value of a molecule is E_1 (which in the simple case we are considering here will correspond to a mean velocity $\bar{v_1}$ with $E_1 = \frac{1}{2}m\overline{v_1^2}$), and another possible value is $E_2 = \frac{1}{2}m\overline{v_2^2}$. Then the probabilities of finding the molecule in each condition are $a \exp\left(-\dfrac{E_1}{kT}\right)$ and $a \exp\left(-\dfrac{E_2}{kT}\right)$ where a is a constant, so that the ratio of these probabilities will be

$$\exp\left(\frac{E_2 - E_1}{kT}\right).$$

For an assembly of a large number of identical molecules, this will give the ratio of the populations of these energy states. The expression is the *Boltzmann distribution*. It is true whatever the nature of the energy E, which may include potential energy as well as kinetic. We will find it useful in discussing molecular amplification (Section 15.4). It is only valid for classical particles, and fails for this reason in the case of electrons in metals (Section 9.20), though it is satisfactory for electrons in non-degenerate semiconductors (Section 10.5).

3.12 **Polyatomic molecules—the principle of equipartition of energy.**   Now since the energy of a gas has so far been considered to be entirely vested in the kinetic energy of the molecules, which we have seen to be $\frac{3}{2}kT$, the derivative of this with respect to room temperature is $\frac{3}{2}k$, or $\frac{3}{2}nk$ per unit volume, which is the specific heat at constant volume, C_v. Experiment indicates that the specific heat of argon is in fact independent of temperature from 90°K upwards; its value is what our discussion would lead us to expect. On the other hand, C_v for nitrogen is greater and increases with rising temperatures. The discrepancy arises because the nitrogen molecule is diatomic, with a 'dumb-bell' form giving an appreciable moment of inertia, and the molecule can store energy as rotation, as well as translation. In fact five terms are now necessary to specify its energy, instead of three for a monatomic gas, and the specific heat is $\frac{5}{2}nk$ instead of $\frac{3}{2}nk$, in accordance with the *principle of equipartition of energy* (Section 14.3).

Because we are dealing with the rotation of an atomic system, classical theory is inadequate, and it is found that the rotational energy is quantized into equidistant discrete levels. If $\frac{1}{2}kT$ is not large compared with the interlevel spacing, all the molecules will be in the ground state and no change of rotational energy with temperature will occur.

In nitrogen at high temperatures, C_v is higher than $\frac{5}{2}nk$, since there is sufficient energy to excite *vibrations* in the molecule, where further energy (again quantized) can be stored.

These extra energy levels associated with vibration and rotation give rise to new lines in the spectra of molecules. As the energy between successive levels is small, the individual lines occur at low frequencies (in the infra-red or microwave region) and the individual lines are often not resolved so that the spectrum appears as broad 'bands'.

A consequence of this continual exchange of energy in the molecule is that kinetic energy transferred to the molecule by a violent collision for example, can be transformed into energy of vibration and rotation quite readily. This is sufficient, in extreme cases, to lead to the disintegration or rearrangement of molecules, and explains the important fact that chemical reactions will often not proceed unless sufficient kinetic energy is available, i.e. at high temperature.

3.13   Electronic and nuclear motion separated.

In treating molecular problems we have a clear example of an element implicit in the argument from the beginning—we have always discussed electronic energy levels assuming that the nuclei in the molecule are stationary, and only in the last paragraph have we added to this the possibility that the nuclei might execute periodic motions of their own. We are justified in separating electronic and nuclear motion in this way because of the great difference in mass between electrons and nuclei. Without this separation any kind of treatment of molecules would be very difficult. We shall return to the point in connection with crystals in Chapter 9.

3.14   Van der Waals force.

The behaviour of gases described by the kinetic theory, even when allowance is made for rotation and vibration of molecules, is still something of an idealization, because we have not allowed for a force of attraction between the molecules other than at the instant of collision. This force causes significant deviations of a real gas from the ideal equation of state $PV = RT$ and, more strikingly, brings about its liquefaction and ultimate solidification. The so-called *van der Waals force* arises as follows. The electrons in an atom are to be thought of as describing orbits about the nucleus, and hence an atom as a whole must have a fluctuating dipole moment, which will induce a corresponding dipole moment in a nearby molecule. This leads to a rather weak force of attraction, which falls off rapidly with distance, and is the van der Waals force. It is responsible for the binding in solidified argon, and in general in those crystals which are built up from molecules rather than from individual atoms.

3.15   The characteristics of crystals.

At sufficiently low temperatures, interatomic forces, whether ionic or covalent or the weaker van der Waals force, will bring about the solidification of matter in an ordered form. The order arises because the energy of the aggregate can be minimized in that way, and this is true whether the forces are directional or not. This atomic regularity is the attribute of the crystalline state, the cause underlying the large scale regularity that ensures, for instance, the uniformity of angles between crystal faces.

If we move from a given point in a crystal (disregarding surfaces) we shall eventually come to an environment identical with that from which we started, and if we continue in the same direction, this situation will be repeated at regular intervals. There are some directions in which these recurrences occur more frequently, and these are a natural choice for *crystal axes*. If on three such axes we mark off the appropriate minimum repeat distance, we shall define a parallelepiped known as the *unit cell* of the crystal, and the crystal can be constructed by the indefinite multiplication of this unit cell (Fig. 3.2(a)). There is only a finite number of possible shapes of cell; the more important cases are those corresponding to crystals of higher symmetry, and these frequently have orthogonal axes.

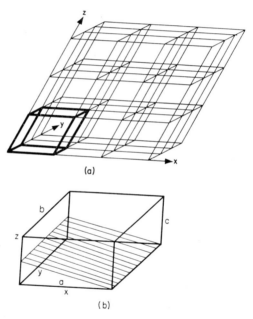

Fig. 3.2 (a) Crystal axes and space lattice showing unit cell.
(b) Rectangular unit cell. The shaded plane has Miller indices (102).

3.16 **Miller indices.** We can define the orientation of any plane—it may be a crystal face—with reference to the unit cell, by considering the intercepts of the plane on the axes, expressed as a fraction of the unit cell dimensions. The reciprocals of these quantities are always found to be small integers for a plane corresponding to a crystal face. These integers (hkl) are referred to as *Miller indices* and are the standard way of specifying crystallographic planes. A simple example is shown on Fig. 3.2(b). The normals to these planes can be similarly designated, but with different brackets [*hkl*].

Note that the consideration of the unit cells tells us nothing about how the individual atoms are arranged inside them. For our purposes, it is the translational symmetry of the crystal which is of importance, and for this the notion of unit cell is sufficient.

3.17　**Metals.**　We can envisage three distinct types of crystal, corresponding to covalent and ionic bonding and to van der Waals forces respectively, but the question now arises, where do the metals fit in our scheme? Bonding due to van der Waals forces is too weak; ionic bonding is clearly out of the question. So, however, is covalent bonding, for metal crystals commonly take a form in which each atom may have twelve equivalent near neighbours, and no arrangement of electron sharing can be devised for so many. We can only conclude that metal crystals cannot be successfully assimilated into our scheme, and at present we can do no better than to consider an aggregate of positive ions, held together by the electrons which are the collective property of the whole crystal. The justification for such a view comes from a different approach to the problem, considered in Chapter 9. Meanwhile, we can regard electrons from the common pool as being released from the crystal if sufficient energy is supplied to it, exactly as a single atom may be ionized. Details of the process will be considered in the next chapter (Chapter 4).

The example will serve as a reminder that to look at molecules and crystals in terms of the disturbed energy levels of the constituent free atoms is an approximation, and clearly one that does not hold for metals.

REFERENCES

SINNOTT, M. J. *The Solid State for Engineers*, Wiley, New York (1958).

PROBLEMS

3.1　The potential energy of a diatomic molecule is given in terms of the interatomic distance r by the expression

$$E = -\frac{A}{r^2} + \frac{B}{r^{10}}$$

where　$A = 1 \cdot 44 \times 10^{-39}$ joule m^2

$B = 2 \cdot 19 \times 10^{-12}$ joule m^{10}

Discuss the significance of the two terms. Calculate the equilibrium separation of the atoms (the separation at which the energy is a minimum) and the dissociation energy (the energy required to separate the atoms to infinity).

3.2 Loschmidt's number, the number of molecules in 1 m³ of an ideal gas at 1 atmosphere pressure and 273°K, is $2 \cdot 6872 \times 10^{25}$ $m^{-3}atm^{-1}$. Calculate the number of molecules/m³ at

(i) 10^{-6} mmHg. and 290°K (a normal 'high vacuum')

(ii) 10^{-10}mm and 290°K (approaching the highest vacuum attainable)

(iii) 2.10^{-4} mmHg. and 200°K (conditions in the atmosphere at an altitude of 100 km — the E-region of the ionosphere)

3.3 Calculate the root-mean-square velocity of (i) hydrogen molecules, (ii) oxygen molecules at a temperature of 17°C. What is the difference between total energy and translational kinetic energy for these molecules?

Discuss the absence of hydrogen from the earth's atmosphere qualitatively in the light of the calculated velocities.

3.4 Suppose the mean molecular diameter of air to be 3×10^{-10}m. To what pressure must a vessel be evacuated if its mean free path is to exceed 10 cm?

3.5 Draw planes having the following Miller indices in relation to a crystal unit cell in the form of a cube: 100; 010; 110; 101; 111; 11$\bar{1}$.

N.B. The notation $\bar{1}$ refers to a Miller index of minus one.

3.6 Germanium forms crystals with a cubic unit cell containing effectively two germanium atoms. The atomic weight of germanium is $72 \cdot 6$, and the density $5 \cdot 460$ gm/cm³. What is the unit cell cube edge?

3.7 The scattering of X-rays of wavelength λ by a crystal lattice may be regarded as reflection from a stack of equally spaced planes, d apart, which are identified with planes of atoms in the lattice. Show that energy reflected from successive planes will be in phase, so giving a diffracted beam of significant intensity, if

$$n\lambda = 2d \sin \alpha \text{ (Bragg's Law)}$$

where α is the angle between the X-ray beam on the plane in question.

The cube edge of the unit cell of sodium chloride has a length of $5 \cdot 627 \times 10^{-10}$m. A beam of copper $K\alpha$ X-rays is diffracted by planes parallel to the cube faces through a minimum angle of 7° 51′. What is the wavelength of the copper $K\alpha$?

Chapter 4

Emission of Electrons from Solids

4.1 **Historical.** Experimental work in the nineteenth century showed that when ultra-violet radiation of short wavelength fell on a metal, it would commonly acquire a positive electric charge, and also that metals heated to a sufficiently high temperature behaved similarly. The results of early investigations were incomplete and even contradictory, and it was only when techniques for investigating the effects in a vacuum were developed that real progress was possible. Experiments carried out by J. J. Thomson showed that when a metal was irradiated with ultra-violet light or heated it emitted electrons, which were identified by their e/m value. These processes and others by which electrons may be released into a vacuum will be considered in this chapter. They are of great practical importance as the indispensible source of the electrons in all vacuum electronic devices. From the practical viewpoint, the emission of electrons from a hot body—*thermionic emission*—is the most important, and it will be considered first.

4.2 **Comparison of thermionic emission and evaporation.** At the outset, we shall compare thermionic emission with evaporation, the evaporation of water for instance. Energy is required to bring about the change from the liquid to the vapour state. This is usually described as a latent heat, 540 cal/g, but we can also express it as the energy required to remove a single molecule of water from the liquid, in which case it is more usefully expressed in electron volts as 0·4 eV. We can now try to interpret the latent heat specifically in terms of the work done against intermolecular forces. The forces are short range in character, so that most of the work of detaching a molecule from the liquid is expended in the early stages.

Within a closed vessel, an equilibrium will be established, when the number of molecules leaving the liquid in this way is just equal to the number of molecules in the vapour which collide with the liquid surface. The number of these collisions depends on the pressure of the vapour, and in this way we can arrive at an expression for the vapour pressure in terms of the latent heat and temperature.

To compute the rate of evaporation from a given liquid surface under specified conditions is much more difficult. It depends on the rate of re-

D

moval of vapour from the vicinity of the surface, which may be diffusive or turbulent; on the amount and nature of other gases present, and on the condition of the liquid surface. No satisfactory theoretical treatment has yet been given.

4.3 **The work function.** It was mentioned at the end of the last chapter that the electrons in a metal crystal can be regarded as the collective property of the crystal as a whole. Now of these electrons, only a small proportion share in the thermal energy of the crystal, for reasons to be discussed in Section 9.20. Of these, some will find themselves in possession of sufficient energy to escape from the crystal, as will water molecules during evaporation.

There is a very important difference between the two cases, which concerns the range of the forces between the electron and the metal. The electron requires a finite energy to overcome the short-range forces due to the crystal. Acquisition of this energy will bring it to a point outside the metal crystal, but only just outside it. If the electron is to be completely freed from the metal, it must be removed further—to an infinite distance in fact. In the case of a water molecule, this presents no problem, for as soon as the molecule is beyond the reach of the short wave intermolecular forces, it experiences no other force. This is not true of the electron, because it possesses a negative charge, and leaves an equal positive charge (the 'image charge') on the metal. The Coulomb force between these is long-range and the work done against the attraction of the image charge is a large part of the total required to free an electron. This total energy, expressed in volts, is known as the *work function*, ϕ.

4.4 **Photoemission.** There is another difference between electron emission and evaporation. We cannot visualize the energy being supplied to a water molecule other than thermally, but energy can be supplied to an electron in a metal by collision with another particle, or with a photon. The latter process is particularly simple in principle. It is known as the *photoelectric effect*, or more simply *photoemission*.

It is clear that photoemission can only take place if the incident photon can supply enough energy to the electron, i.e. if

$$h\nu \geqslant e\phi,$$

or more precisely if

$$h\nu = e\phi + \tfrac{1}{2}mv^2,$$

an expression due to Einstein which explicitly states that the energy excess appears as kinetic energy of the emitted electrons. If this is correct, there will be a certain minimum frequency for a given metal, below which no photoemission is observed. This limit is quite independent of intensity, for while an increased light intensity will produce more photoelectrons above the threshold, it will release none below it.

This simple principle is of particular importance, because it summarizes the behaviour actually found in photoemission experiments. Obvious as it seems in terms of quantum theory, it is quite impossible to accommodate it in a purely classical theory of radiation, and it played an important part in bringing about the widespread acceptance of quantum theory.

4.5 **Contact difference of potential.** The work function can be expected to vary from one metal to another, and this has an important consequence. If two metals are brought into contact, then from the nature of the work function, the electrons in one metal will have an energy different from those in the other, so that a flow of electrons will commence, to be halted by the charge imbalance which this flow creates. The potential difference set up in this way is the *contact difference of potential* (or contact potential) and its magnitude is given by

$$V_{ab} = \phi_a - \phi_b.$$

4.6 **Determination of work function from photoelectric threshold.** The determination of the photoelectric threshold provides a means of measuring the work function. A plate of the metal under investigation is enclosed in a vacuum vessel which contains also an electrode to collect the emitted electrons. The test surface is irradiated with light whose frequency is changed, and the maximum kinetic energy of the emitted electrons is determined at each frequency from the retarding potential that has to be applied to the collector to reduce the current to it to zero. A linear relationship is obtained between energy and frequency, whose intercept gives the work function. (A correction has to be made for the work function of the anode). In accurate work it is necessary to correct for the temperature of the material, since an increase in the thermal energy of the electrons will effectively reduce the work function as here determined.

Typical values of the work function are given in the table:

Metal	Work function (volts)
Cs	1·9
Na	2·29
Zn	4·24
W	4·49
Fe	4·63
Ag	4·74
Cu	4·86
Pt	6·30

It will be seen that for the alkali metals, the threshold frequency lies in the visible region of the spectrum (roughly from 4000 to 7300 Å) but that for other metals, it is in the ultra-violet.

4.7 **Photoelectric yield.** At frequencies greater than the threshold, the photocurrent, which may be most usefully expressed as the *yield* of electrons per photon, increases to a maximum and then falls off at high frequencies. The shape of the curves depends very much on factors such as the polarization of the incident beam and its angle of incidence. Typically yields are in the region 10^{-4} to 10^{-2} electrons per photon.

4.8 **Effect of surface contamination.** Another most important factor is this: experimental values for both yield and threshold are found to be very variable, even when great pains are taken to ensure reproducible conditions. The divergencies appear to be due to the contamination of the photoemissive surface by residual gas molecules in the vacuum. (It is worth remembering that if a perfectly clean surface was exposed in an ordinary good vacuum of 10^{-6} mmHg a monolayer of gas will be *adsorbed* on it in 1 sec.)

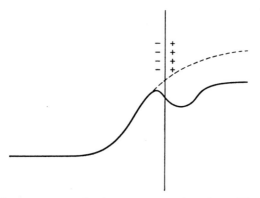

Fig. 4.1 Electron energy level near a crystal surface. The dotted line shows conditions for a clean surface. A monatomic layer of suitable im-purity can lead to a dipole layer as shown, whose potential changes the electron energy to the full line curve, and so reduces the work function. (From Dow W. G. *Fundamentals of Engineering Electronics*, 1st edn., Wiley, New York (1937).)

The importance of this kind of contamination arises when the process of adsorption leads to electron transfer between the adsorbed atoms and the surface layer. Figure 4.1 shows how the ensuing dipole layer changes the effective work function.

All electron emission processes are sensitive to surface contamination of this kind. It is often troublesome, but can also be turned to good account in achieving, by careful treatment, a very efficient surface. (See Sections 4.14, 4.17 and 4.18.)

4.9   **The 'vapour pressure' of electrons.**   Knowing the work function of a metal, we can calculate the equilibrium between electrons in the metal, and the density of thermionic electrons in a cavity in the metal. The calculation is identical with the calculation for the vapour pressure over water mentioned in Section 4.2. This gives the 'vapour pressure' of the electrons. It does not correspond to an observable quantity, but it can be related to the thermionic current density $\mathcal{J}_s$ by equating to the latter an expression, derived from the kinetic theory of gases, for the collision rate of electrons with the metal surface, which itself contains the pressure. We are left with

$$\mathcal{J}_s = \frac{4\pi m \mathbf{k}^2 e}{h^3} \, T^2 \exp\left(-\frac{\phi e}{\mathbf{k}T}\right).$$

This result was first deduced by Richardson. As in the case of evaporation of water from a free surface, it is more difficult to calculate the net electron current from a surface, where there is no thermal equilibrium. It is common practice to apply the Richardson equation to this case also, but in general we do not know that an electron striking the surface of the emitter will necessarily be transmitted; in general it will not, and we do not know what the reflection coefficient is. Furthermore, a real surface will not have a uniform work function, particularly if the metal is polycrystalline, so that ϕ is hard to define. On the other hand, it is easy to measure the electron current from such a surface, and in any case this is the quantity which is closest to our practical interest in thermionic emission. Therefore we can measure the current of thermionic electrons *in vacuo* which flows from a hot body (usually an electrically heated filament) to a collecting electrode, and if we regard the Richardson equation as purely empirical, we shall find that we can fit the data to it quite well. Of course it is no longer possible to interpret the parameters in the way we can in the equilibrium case, but having determined the parameters for a given surface, we can calculate the electron emission at any temperature from tables (see for instance those in Nottingham's article quoted at the end of this chapter).

If we write

$$I_s = AT^2 \exp\left(-\phi/\mathbf{k}T\right),$$

where A is to be determined by experiment, then A is found to be between 4×10^5 and 7×10^5 amp/m² (°K)² for most metals, compared with the value $1 \cdot 2 \times 10^6$ amp/m² (°K)² calculated from the Richardson equation.

4.10   **The role of the collector.**   In making measurements of thermionic current, the collector does not necessarily play only the passive role that its name implies. There are three ways in particular in which conditions at the collector can influence results.

The first of these occurs when the collector is at a negative potential with respect to the emitter, so that electrons only reach it by overcoming a retarding potential, and only those electrons which have enough kinetic energy will be collected. If I_0 is the maximum current that can be collected (the saturation current) it is found that the current I collected with a retarding potential V is such that its natural logarithm is a linear function of V, with a gradient e/kT. In other words

$$(I/I_0) = \exp(-eV/kT).$$

This provides us with a method of determining the temperature of the emitter, but more important, it indicates that the energy distribution of the electrons outside the emitter is given by the Boltzmann function. In other words, the electron 'gas' behaves like the assembly of classical particles presupposed by the kinetic theory of gases, which brings us back to the fundamental point of Thomson's discovery (Section 1.3), but from a different angle.

When $\log I$ is plotted against V in the way just discussed, it is found that the graph is only a straight line when the current is small. At higher currents, there will be a substantial number of electrons in transit between emitter and collector, and the mutual repulsion of the electrons in this *space charge* exerts a major influence on the current. This situation is of fundamental importance in the practical operation of electron devices, and it will be discussed in detail in Chapter 6.

Thirdly, when the collector is maintained at a positive potential, the collector current should be determined only by the emitter temperature and if the collector voltage is sufficient to render space charge effects unimportant, the current—saturation current—should be independent of collector voltage. This is not normally the case, because there is now a point at a finite distance from the emitter surface, at which the force due to image charge is just compensated by the force due to the positive charge on the collector. The electron will be 'free' when it reaches that point, and this is equivalent to a reduction in the work function (Fig. 4.2).

Let the point in question be a distance x_0 from the emitter. The magnitude of the image force at x_0 is

$$\frac{e^2}{16\pi\varepsilon_0 x_0^2},$$

and for exact compensation of the force on the electron at x_0

$$\frac{e^2}{16\pi\varepsilon_0 x_0^2} = eF;$$

whence

$$x_0 = \tfrac{1}{2}\sqrt{\frac{e}{4\pi\varepsilon_0 F}}.$$

Since to escape the electron has only to reach x_0, the work done against the image force will be reduced by

$$\int_{x_0}^{\infty} \frac{e^2}{16\pi\varepsilon_0 x^2}\, dx = \frac{e^2}{16\pi\varepsilon_0 x_0} = \sqrt{\frac{e^2 F}{16\pi\varepsilon_0}} = ex_0 F,$$

and so less energy will be needed for an electron to escape. This is accentuated by the energy $ex_0 F$ gained from the applied field while travelling to x_0. The sum of these two amounts to a reduction in work function given by

$$\phi' = \phi - \sqrt{\frac{eF}{4\pi\varepsilon_0}};$$

hence to obtain the true value of ϕ we must plot ϕ' against F and extrapolate to $F = 0$. This is known as the *Schottky effect*.

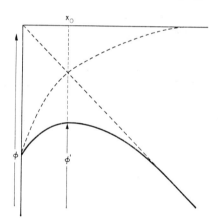

FIG. 4.2 Showing the influence of an applied field on an electron outside a crystal (dotted line) counteracting the influence of image charge (dotted curve) and leading to a reduction in work function $\phi - \phi'$ (full line curve).

4.11 **Practical thermionic emitters.** For a workable vacuum electronic device, there will necessarily be minimum requirements on its power output, and this generally means that we shall require to draw an electron current of the order milliamps or more. This figure is impossible to achieve by photoemissive means, but is attainable by thermionic emission, by going to a sufficiently high temperature. A suitable emitter will be a good conductor that gives the required current density without melting, and without appreciable evaporation of atoms from the solid. Some 'figures of merit' defined as T_p/ϕ where T_p is the temperature at which the vapour pressure is 10^{-5} mmHg, are given in the table.

Metal	T_p (°K)	ϕ (Volts)	T_p/ϕ (°K/V)
W	2860	4·5	638
Th	1910	3·4	563
Na	440	2·3	192
Thoriated tungsten	1910	2·7	710
Oxide cathode	1000	1·5	660

(From Thomson, J. and Callick, E. B. *Electron Physics and Technology*, The English Universities Press, 1959.)

Only the most refractory metals are suitable; platinum may be used, but tungsten is more satisfactory, although it must be operated at temperatures in excess of 2000°K. These temperatures can be attained in a vacuum envelope by using the metal in the form of a wire, and heating it electrically. There are drawbacks to this, notably that a considerable power consumption is needed to maintain the required temperature, energy losses from the filament by radiation being very great. This makes the efficiency (work function/energy expended per electron emitted) of this kind of emitter very low. In addition, it is desirable in any electronic device that the electrons should be emitted from an equipotential surface, and this is impossible in a wire heated electrically.

4.12 **Thoriated tungsten.** It is a difficult metallurgical problem to draw tungsten wires of the kind demanded for these thermionic filaments, but it was discovered that the addition of a small amount of thorium as oxide improved the ductility considerably. Langmuir and Rogers, investigating the properties of this thoriated tungsten in 1913, found that the electron emission was higher than that of pure tungsten by a factor of 10^5. This was interpreted as due to the decomposition of the thorium oxide to produce a thorium monolayer at the surface of the tungsten, giving rise to the kind of dipole layer mentioned in Section 4.8 which will reduce the effective work function. Although loss of thorium by evaporation from the monolayer is significant, it will be replaced by diffusion from below.

It is also known that small concentrations of oxygen will seriously inhibit electron emission from tungsten, and this is attributed to the formation of a monolayer of the opposite polarity.

The great advantage of a thoriated tungsten cathode is that it can be operated at much lower temperatures than the equivalent cathode of pure tungsten.

4.13   **The oxide cathode.**   A further advance, of even greater practical importance, was the discovery by Wehnelt that a metal surface coated with oxides of the alkaline earth metals (calcium, barium or strontium), can be an even more efficient electron emitter, after suitable heat treatment. An 'oxide cathode' can therefore be operated at lower temperatures (below $1100°K$), and it is now feasible to coat a tubular metal former with the oxide, and heat it indirectly from a central heater wire. The emitting surface can now be made an equipotential.

To prepare an oxide cathode the materials—usually a mixture of alkaline earths—are used in the form of carbonates, ground to a paste with an organic binding material. This is sprayed onto the former, usually a nickel alloy, mounted in the electrode structure of the valve, and heated gently while the valve is still attached to the vacuum pumps. At this stage the binder is volatilized and the carbonates are decomposed to the oxides. The oxides themselves are unstable in moist air, so that this indirect method of preparation is necessary. After the decomposition a process of *activation* is necessary to produce an efficient thermionic emitter. This process usually takes the form of heating to a temperature above the intended operating temperature, while emission current is simultaneously drawn.

The oxide cathode is the standard electron source in vacuum electronic devices, and is used whenever its disadvantages do not make this impossible. These disadvantages arise from the low mechanical strength of the oxide layer, which cause it to flake off when used under extreme conditions. Also, the inhomogeneous nature of the oxide material can also lead to the development of local 'hotspots' at high emission densities, followed by rapid deterioration. For this reason thoriated tungsten cathodes are employed in large transmitting valves for use at low frequencies, and in the largest valves (H.T. voltages above 15 kV) pure tungsten cathodes are used. The high temperature at which the latter operate means that there will be considerable thermal distortion of the valve structure, and this type of cathode can only be used where the interelectrode spacing of the valve is sufficiently large.

4.14   **The operation of the oxide cathode.**   There is still no satisfactory understanding of the operation of the oxide cathode. The conductivity of the oxide is assured at high temperature by its semiconducting nature. The porous structure of the polycrystalline oxide gives a very large effective surface area from which emission can take place, and the activation procedure probably modifies the properties of this surface to lower the work function. Detailed mechanisms of the processes concerned are still unresolved problems.

The baneful influence of oxygen in 'poisoning' cathode surfaces has been mentioned. To remove oxygen by pumping out during the manufacture of the valve is insufficient, because slow release of oxygen into the vaccuum will subsequently take place. Steps are therefore taken to remove this oxygen chemically as and when it is evolved by arranging to deposit a film of metallic barium on part of the inner surface of the valve envelope just after pumping—a process known as 'gettering'.

4.15   **The dispenser cathode.**   Both the thoriated tungsten and the oxide cathode depend for their success on the maintenance of special conditions at the emitter surface, and this is achieved in both cases by the existence of a reservoir of active material in the bulk of the cathode. The most recent development in the way of a practical cathode makes a very direct use of the same principle and the *dispenser cathode* consists of a matrix of porous tungsten, whose pores contain a mixture of barium and strontium oxides, which can diffuse to the surface. Very high emission currents can be drawn, no doubt because the oxide layer can constantly be replaced. Also, the cathode can be produced by pressing and sintering prior to assembly in the valve, and can be ground to the close tolerances required in planar triodes (Section 6.14), for instance. This kind of cathode is very valuable in high frequency applications, particularly in connection with travelling-wave tubes (Section 6.16).

4.16   **The direct conversion of heat energy to electricity.**   A thermionic emitter heated non-electrically provides a possible alternative to the steam cycle in the production of electrical power, and a considerable research effort is at present devoted to this. The problem is in great measure a matter of finding a material with good thermionic properties which can be effectively heated by conventional or nuclear fuel.

The maximum thermionic current cannot normally be drawn from a device of this kind since space charge (Section 4.10) will limit the current flowing from the thermionic cathode. If the space charge can be neutralized by positive gaseous ions as it is in the thyratron (Section 7.7), this limitation is removed. This is the principle of the *plasma diode*, a device with considerable, but still unrealized, potentialities.

4.17 **Practical photocathodes.** Since both thermionic emission and photoemission depend on the value of the work function, the requirements for efficiency are the same for each, though the means of attaining them will be different.

Photoemissive devices are required to transfer a signal from optical to electrical form, whether the application is a simple light-actuated relay or a television camera tube. Response in the visible region of the spectrum is usually required. The alkali metals have a suitable threshold for these applications, but their yield is very poor ($\sim 10^{-3}$ electrons/photon). Caesium is effective in more complex cathodes, however. For instance a silver substrate may be oxidized, and a layer of caesium deposited on the oxide to produce an emitter of higher yield (0·2 electrons/photon). Alternatively, the caesium may be deposited on a thin layer of antimony or bismuth; oxygen treatment is again important. The wavelength response of the former is shown in Fig. 4.3. The 'tri-alkali' cathode consists of sodium, potassium and caesium deposited on antimony. It has a wavelength response closely matched to that of the eye, and is important in television camera tubes (Section 5.1) and similar applications.

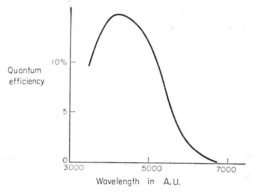

Fig. 4.3 The quantum efficiency of an SbCsO photocathode at different wavelengths. (Adapted from Gibbons D. J. 'The tri-alkali stabilized CPI emitron', in *Advances in Electronics and Electron Physics*, Vol. 12, Academic Press, New York (1960).)

Cathodes of this type may be deposited on glass in a semi-transparent form so that the light can be incident from one side and the electrons emitted on the other. It is not yet clear whether the operation of these surfaces depends on the formation of semiconducting compounds or whether individual adsorbed caesium atoms are effective, by virtue of the special properties of the substrate.

4.18 **Secondary electron emission.** If an electron of sufficient energy strikes the surface of a conductor, the energy may be lost by the expulsion of other electrons from the conductor—δ secondaries for each primary, where δ is defined as the *yield*. This is particularly important in connection with photoemission, since the small photocurrents obtainable can be amplified if the electrons are first accelerated and made to strike a *dynode* where secondary emission can take place. A series of such stages in cascade are usually employed in a *photomultiplier*; with 11 stages an amplification of 10^7 in photocurrent can be obtained, corresponding to a δ of between 4 and 5 per stage. Once again work function is the determining factor, and a compound surface is found to be more efficient than a pure metal, a deposit of caesium on an oxidized silver substrate being commonly used for photomultiplier dynodes. For electron multiplication in demountable equipment, where the dynodes must be exposed to air, an alloy of beryllium and copper is often used; there is evidence that an oxide layer is necessary for its efficient functioning.

The multiplication of thermionically emitted electrons has not been achieved on a practically useful basis, because the thermionic cathode 'poisons' the dynodes. Secondary emission as a troublesome effect on tetrodes will be discussed in Section 6.10.

Closely related is the emission of electrons by a metal under positive ion bombardment. This is important as a sustaining process in gas discharges, and as the source of electrons in *cold cathode tubes*. The electron emission in these cases need not necessarily be due to ions; excited atoms of long lifetime (metastables) may be equally effective (see Section 7.17).

REFERENCES

NOTTINGHAM, W. B. 'Thermionic emission' in *Encyclopaedia of Physics*, vol. 21, Springer, Berlin (1956).

PROBLEMS

4.1 A certain photosensitive surface has a work function of 2·5 volts. What is the threshold wavelength? What is the energy of the fastest photoelectrons emitted if the surface is exposed to ultraviolet radiation of 2536 Å wavelength?

4.2 A photocathode is 1 m distant from a 100 watt sodium lamp (monochromatic emission 5890 Å). The quantum yield at this wavelength is 3%. What is the photoelectric current density?

4.3 The cathode of a diode is 2 cm long, and has a diameter of 0·05 mm. The saturation current I is observed at different cathode temperatures T, and zero field values I_0 are obtained by extrapolation to eliminate the Schottky effect. Log (I_0/T^2) is plotted against $1/T$. A linear plot is obtained, whose gradient is $1 \cdot 16 \times 10^4$. The intercept at $1/T = 0$ is $2 \cdot 26 \times 10^{-3}$. Find the values of A and ϕ when the equation at the end of Section 4.9 is applied to this cathode. How would you measure the temperature of the cathode?

4.4 The work function of a clean metal surface is ϕ_0. The surface is covered with a monatomic film of N atoms/m², each atom contributing an orientated dipole of moment M at the surface. Show that the work function will be modified to

$$\phi = \phi_0 + NM/\varepsilon_0$$

where ε_0 is the dielectric constant of free space. Give the sense of the dipole layer required to reduce ϕ.

4.5 A hot cathode will lose energy by radiation; in a particular instance the rate of loss is found to be $0 \cdot 4$ times that of a 'black body' at the same temperature, which radiates energy at a rate

$$5 \cdot 73 \times 10^{-8} \times T^4 \text{ watt/m}^2$$

A tungsten cathode is run at 2300°K, and the electrons leaving it have an average total energy of $0 \cdot 2$ eV. Compare the rate of loss of energy due to the electron emission (the 'latent heat of evaporation' of the electrons) with the energy loss by radiation.

4.6 The emission of a cathode at 2100°K decreases by 5% over a certain time interval. What change of work function does this represent? If the field strength at the cathode in normal operation is 10^4 volt/m, to what extent must the field be increased to restore the emission to its original value?

4.7 The sensitivity of the cathode of a photomultiplier tube of 13 stages is 50 μamp/lumen. At an applied H.T. of 150 volts per stage the overall sensitivity is 10,000 amp/lumen. What is the value of δ for each stage?

Chapter 5

Electron Optics

5.1 **Introduction.** The title of this chapter follows from the duality of matter and radiation discussed in Chapter 2. If, for instance, we were pressed to explain the physical significance of a ray diagram in optics, we should naturally think of the ray as being the envelope of the normals to a wavefront, although it would be equally valid to speak of the ray as the trajectory of a photon. In dealing with electrons, it is less easy to keep the wave and particle interpretations distinct, so the hybrid title is appropriate.

Basically, in this chapter we are interested in establishing the trajectories of electrons in electric and magnetic fields. Starting from the idea of the electron as a particle, we shall find similarities between the effects of these fields on the trajectory and the influence of a refractive medium on a light ray, and shall find it expedient to think of electron *lenses*, and even entire electron-optical instruments. We can push the analogy even further, from geometrical to physical optics, by considering the resolution of optical instruments in terms of waves, electromagnetic and de Broglie respectively.

It may be mentioned here that we are concerned with electron motion only in electromagnetic fields, with no complicating features. This presupposes, in this chapter and the two which follow, the existence of a high vacuum technique which will enable us to construct apparatus in which the electrons complete their paths without significant collisions. The fact that we shall take this for granted hereafter does not detract from its importance.

Many examples would serve to illustrate the argument. We choose to stress one—the cathode ray oscillograph—because of its intrinsic importance. Other matters are discussed very briefly, and for the sake of completeness only.

5.2 **The electron beam as a measuring instrument.** The determination of e/m for electrons, carried out by J. J. Thomson and described in Chapter 1, makes use of a beam of electrons which is deflected by known electric and magnetic fields, the deflection being observable because the electron beam produces a patch of fluorescence where it impinges on the glass wall of the vacuum vessel.

The same procedure can be used in reverse, once e/m is known, to determine an unknown electrical potential difference applied to the deflecting plates, or an unknown current through the electromagnetic coils. This measuring instrument has two substantial advantages. First, the electron beam has a very low inertia compared with a pointer or even with the mirror of an optical lever, so that rapidly fluctuating phenomena can be investigated—and, second, in the case of potential measurement, the input impedance will be high, depending only on the capacitance of the deflecting plates. An electron device designed for this purpose is a *cathode ray oscillograph*. Its action depends on guiding the motion of a substantial number of electrons along a single trajectory. The actual number of electrons in the beam is of secondary importance, just as an account of image formation in a telescope can be given without discussing the brightness of the image formed. This analogy, casually drawn between electron motion and geometrical optics, is a most important one, as the title of this chapter would imply. Our discussion of the behaviour of electrons in a vacuum will start with this topic.

5.3 **The cathode ray oscillograph—principles of operation.** Despite what has just been said, it is clear that the number of electrons in the beam must be sufficient to produce a spot bright enough to see, or, if the beam current is to be measured directly by collecting the electrons in a Faraday can, the current must be large enough to measure. The latter procedure is, of course, intolerably clumsy, and the chance observation that cathode rays produce fluorescence in glass provides a direct and elegant method for detecting the position of the beam which has been used ever since. The fluorescence can be looked upon as a means of converting electrical energy into light, so that the location can be perceived directly. As it stands, the process in glass is a very inefficient one, but materials do exist—willemite (zinc silicate) or mixtures of zinc and cadmium sulphides and selenides with small quantities of specific impurities, such as copper—which will operate at an efficiency as high as 25 per cent. Materials of this kind (phosphors) can be deposited as a thin layer of microcrystalline powder on the inside of the glass envelope of the cathode ray tube. A feature of phosphors is the decay of the glow produced by electron impact, after the impact has ceased. The decay time may be as short as 10^{-4} sec or as long as the order of minutes. Long persistance traces are valuable in the study of recurrent phenomena of long period, as in some radar applications.

5.4 **The cathode ray oscillograph—practical requirements.** Granted, then, that we can make the electron beam visible, how are we to use it as a measuring instrument? The problems which arise in accom-

plishing this will provide us with a sufficient introduction to the technique
of guiding a stream of electrons along a given path. More complex examples will be mentioned briefly at the end of the chapter. Let us consider
the essentials of a useful cathode ray oscillograph.

First, the electron beam must contain sufficient electrons, of sufficient
energy to produce enough quanta of visible light per second to be visible.
This requires a certain beam current and a certain accelerating potential.
Second, the field between the deflection plates must be sufficient to deflect
the beam by a detectable amount i.e. the sensitivity must be adequate.
Finally, it will be easier to satisfy the second requirement if the beam is
sharp, i.e. the area of electron impacts on the screen is as small as possible.

In addition, we shall usually require some second deflecting agency to
represent an independent variable, which in the study of fluctuating
phenomena is usually time. This gives the electron beam a uniformly increasing x deflection while the signal to be studied gives a deflection in the y
direction, so producing a graph of the signal as a function of time, which in
the case of a periodic signal, can be made recurrent by a *time base* circuit.
Finally, since it will be seen the potential required to deflect the electron
beam is high, it will generally be necessary to amplify the input. These and
other circuits included in the oscillograph, important as they are, are outside our scope and will not be discussed. It is the cathode ray tube itself
that concerns us here, and the components of this tube can be discussed in
terms of electron beam formation, deflection and utilization.

5.5 The deflection of an electron beam by an electric field.
Consider deflection first as a simple example. If we have a beam of electrons
moving in a field-free space at potential V_1, let us investigate the effect on
their motion on passing into a second field-free space at potential V_2.

At the boundary there must be a potential gradient, i.e. a field which
will accelerate the electron in a direction perpendicular to the boundary.
The velocity parallel to the boundary will not be changed. If the angle
between the trajectory and the normal to the boundary is θ_1, the electron
will leave the boundary at a corresponding angle θ_2 (Fig. 5.1) where,
equating components parallel to the boundary

$$v_1 \sin \theta_1 = v_2 \sin \theta_2,$$

v_1 and v_2 being the electron velocities in the two regions.

If we reckon the electron energies in terms of an electron at rest at zero
potential, then since $eV = \frac{1}{2} mv^2$,

$$v_1 \propto \sqrt{V_1}, \quad v_2 \propto \sqrt{V_2},$$

and
$$\frac{\sin \theta_1}{\sin \theta_2} = \sqrt{\frac{V_2}{V_1}}.$$

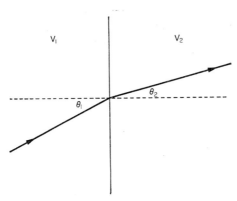

FIG. 5.1   The 'refraction' of an electron trajectory at an interface between regions of different potential.

This is analogous to the law of refraction of a light ray at the interface between media, with $\sqrt{(V_2/V_1)}$ playing the part of refractive index. By changing the potentials the 'refractive index' can be varied. We can therefore use the principles of geometrical optics to plot electron paths through a series of regions at different potentials, and by choosing regions suitably we are able to 'focus' a beam and arrange for its subsequent deflection. Thus a curved interface between equipotential areas will act as a lens. Figure 5.2 shows a simple electrostatic lens and representative trajectories of electrons through it are indicated.

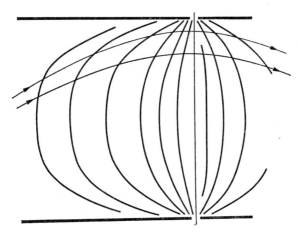

FIG. 5.2   A simple electron lens—the gap between identical cylinders at potentials $+V$ and $-V$ respectively. Equipotential lines around the gap are shown (the configuration is symmetrical about the gap). Sample trajectories show the converging action of the lens. (Adapted from Spangenberg, K.R. *Vacuum Tubes*, McGraw-Hill, New York (1948).)

E

It will be noted that in light optics an abrupt interface between two media is usual, but in electron optics it is exceptional. The deflecting plates of J. J. Thomson's experiment acts as a region of changing refractive index. It can be seen from Fig. 5.2 that the refraction is most pronounced when the potential changes most rapidly. This indicates the rather different ways in which identical optical *principles* are applied in electron and light optics.

5.6 **The electron gun.** These principles can be used to produce a beam of electrons with the electron 'gun' shown in Fig. 5.3. Electrons are emitted from a cathode C in the form of an oxide-covered disc (a button cathode), indirectly heated from behind, and surrounded by a cylindrical

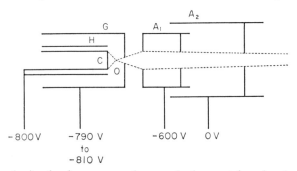

FIG. 5.3 A simple electron gun for a cathode ray tube, showing typical operating potentials for the electrodes. The extent of the electron beam and the position O of the 'crossover point' are indicated. (From Spangenberg, K.R. *Vacuum Tubes*, McGraw-Hill, New York (1948).)

heat shield H to improve the thermal efficiency. The cylinder G adjacent to it is maintained at a negative potential which controls the space charge of the emitted electrons at C (see Section 6.2) and hence controls the emission current, fulfilling the same purpose as the grid in a triode valve. In addition to this, with the second cylinder A_1 it forms a converging electron lens which causes the trajectories of electrons from the cathode to cross over at a point on the axis, and subsequently diverge. Hence, although electrons are emitted in all directions from the surface of the cathode, a substantial proportion of them appear to diverge from the point O, and it is O which is the object of the equivalent optical system. A third cylinder A_2 forms with A_1 a second electron lens which produces an image of the crossover point, and this is arranged to coincide with the screen, so that the ultimate size of the spot is as small as possible.

5.7 **The role of aperture stops.** Because the crossover point is in fact a diminished image of the electron source, there is no need for the latter to be small, so that it is not difficult to obtain a substantial beam current without having to pay too high a price in the way of ultimate spot size. The cylinders A_1 and A_2 carry limiting diaphragms, as Fig. 5.3 shows. These are not themselves very important in the process of focusing, but they serve to limit the electron beam so that only those trajectories almost parallel to the axis are included, in the same way that aperture stops are used in optical instruments to reduce aberrations. Aberrations in the electron gun of the cathode ray tube give rise to loss of definition of the spot when it is deflected, and to a change of spot size with beam intensity. In practice A_2 can be split so that the crossover point can be screened from A_1, whose potential is normally varied to control the focus. Otherwise there is an undesirable interaction between the focus control (which adjusts the potential of A_1) and the brilliance control (which adjusts the potential of G).

5.8 **High-current beams.** How far is it possible to go on increasing the beam current without loss of focus, i.e. to increase the current *density* in the beam? There are two difficulties here. First, the electrons leave the cathode in all directions, and with a distribution of velocities; Fig. 5.4 shows the effect of electrons leaving a point on the filament with opposite tangential directions. Because of the non-zero velocity with which the electrons leave the cathode, the trajectories will be as shown in the diagram, and will lead to an enlargement of the crossover region. It can be shown that the current density in the beam can be increased only by simultaneously increasing the size of the crossover region. If part of the region is selected

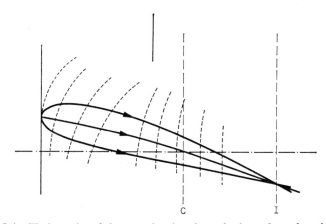

FIG. 5.4   Trajectories of electrons leaving the cathode surface of an electron gun tangentially, but in opposite directions. The paths intersect at a point, which lies on the image plane of the cathode. To obtain the best spot, neither the cathode nor its image I should be focused on the fluorescent screen, but the 'cross-over point' C where the paths cross the axis. The diameter of the electron beam is at its minimum at that point. (Adapted from Spangenberg, K.R. *Vacuum Tubes*, McGraw-Hill, New York (1948).)

by a limiting aperture, the increase in current density will be useful in producing a brighter but still well-defined spot on the screen, but only at the cost of wasting an increasing proportion of the total emission from the cathode.

The second factor which must be considered is the repulsive force of the electrons in the beam on each other, which will cause an initially parallel beam to diverge, and so will effectively defocus the spot. Little has been done to deal with this problem within the field of cathode ray tube design, but in relation to other applications of electron beams the problem has been considered, notably by Pierce, and suitable electron guns have been designed on a new principle. Consider electron flow in a planar diode under conditions of space charge limitation (Section 6.2). The path of each electron will be a straight line, because interactions of the electron with its neighbours must average to zero perpendicular to this line, from the symmetry of the problem. These idealized conditions can be simulated in an electron beam if the gun electrodes are so shaped as to produce a potential distribution identical with the planar case. In velocity modulated valves (Chapter 6) there is a need for an electron beam of high density, going well beyond the requirements of the cathode ray tube in this direction, and for this application the 'Pierce cathode' provides a practical solution. Other kinds of cathodes which have been developed with this end in view are discussed in Reference 3 at the end of the chapter.

5.9 **Sensitivity of deflecting plates.** To return to the cathode ray tube, having produced an electron beam as compact and as dense as required, it is necessary to deflect it—usually to apply separate deflecting forces in two perpendicular directions. This is commonly done, in oscilloscope practice, by electrostatic fields between suitably placed parallel plates in the stem of the tube. This simple arrangement has a number of limitations. The maximum deflection of the beam which can be produced is limited by the beam's striking the edge of the deflecting plates, and if this is countered by increasing the plate separation, the field produced by a given signal voltage decreases, and the sensitivity falls. If, on the other hand, the separation is kept constant but the length of the deflecting plates is decreased, sensitivity is again lost, because the electron is only exposed to the deflecting field for a shorter time.

Even apart from these limitations, the parallel plate arrangement is not ideal because, as the electron moves through the region between the plates, the deflecting force is not uniform since only the component normal to the motion is effective, and this will change along the curved trajectory of the deflected beam. The result will be a distortion of the image on the screen (trapezium distortion). Clearly what is required is a pair of deflecting plates shaped so that the component of the field normal to the trajectory remains the same, and this calls for curved plates, whose profile can be calculated. In practice, for ease of manufacture, this curvature can be approximated sufficiently accurately by one or more straight but divergent sections, as shown in Fig. 5.5. This arrangement has the advantage of increasing the usable screen area for a given spacing and length of the deflecting plates. It is also common practice to flare the plates in width, so as to reduce the plate area to a minimum, because redundant plate area will increase the interplate capacity.

Another form of distortion will occur if the potential of one of a pair of

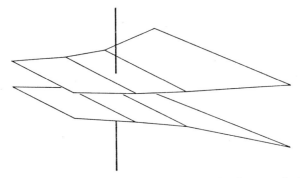

F IG . 5.5   Flared plates to eliminate distortion in the electrostatic deflection of an electron beam.

deflecting plates is not symmetrical with respect to the other, since electrons passing closer to the high potential plate will be accelerated preferentially. This can be avoided by arranging a balanced output from the amplifier so that the *mean* potential of the plates does not change.

5.10   **Post-deflection acceleration.**   The brightness of the final image can be increased not only by increasing the beam current density, the possibilities of which have already been explored, but also by increasing the energy of each electron by an increase in the accelerating voltage. Unfortunately, this is an expedient which reduces the sensitivity of the deflecting system, which is inversely proportional to the electron energy (see Section 1.2). This can be avoided if the electron beam can be accelerated additionally *after* deflection. This so-called post-deflection acceleration (PDA) can be accomplished by coating the inside of the cathode ray tube with a conducting layer (usually graphite), which is brought, via an external pin, to a return circuit. This coating can then be maintained at a potential necessary to accelerate the beam after it leaves the deflecting plates. Unfortunately, the gun electrode A_2 and the graphite film constitute an electron lens which is invariably converging, so that it acts in such a way as to reduce the deflection of the beam, and some of the extra sensitivity which it was the object of the PDA to achieve is lost. If the graphite layer is made in the form of a helix, and the accelerating potential is applied across the ends of it, the electron will be subject to a uniform accelerating field, and will be free from this defect, and this is in fact the normal practice.

The arrangement of a typical tube with PDA is shown in Fig. 5.6, in which the potentials applied to the various electrodes are given.

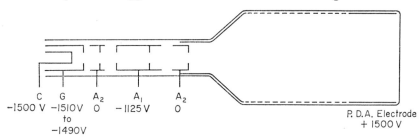

FIG. 5.6   Electrode arrangement in a cathode ray tube with PDA. The deflecting plates are not shown but would be situated at the extreme right-hand end of the neck of the tube. The graphite helix on the tube is shown in section (dotted); it is connected to A_2. The labelling of the electrodes follows Fig. 5.3, but A_2 is split as discussed in Section 5.7. Typical operating potentials are given. (From Spangenberg, K.R. *Vacuum Tubes*, McGraw-Hill, New York (1948).)

5.11   **Conditions at the phosphor screen.**   It remains to consider what happens to the electron beam on striking the phosphor layer on the screen—remembering that the phosphor, like the glass on which it is deposited, is an insulator. One would expect the insulator to charge up until it attains a negative potential sufficient to repel the electrons in the beam, but we must also consider the emission of electrons by secondary emission discussed in the last chapter (Section 4.18). The screen will reach an equilibrium in which the rate of arrival of primary electrons will be just balanced by the departure of secondaries. Since the yield of secondary electrons depends on the energy of the primaries, the potential of the screen, at the point where the beam strikes it, will adjust itself so that the equilibrium is established—to what is called the *sticking potential*. The secondary electrons are collected on the graphite lining of the tube. A high sticking potential will substantially retard the electrons in the beam, with consequent loss in brightness, and it is a common practice to evaporate a thin layer of aluminium behind the phosphor layer on the screen. This prevents the attainment of a high sticking potential but is still thin enough to transmit the primary beam. It has the additional effect of providing a reflecting optical backing to the phosphor layer, so that a considerably greater part of the light produced passes usefully towards the observer's eye.

5.12 **Storage tubes and television camera tubes.**   In the cathode ray tube we have seen how the electron beam, falling on the phosphor layer which is an insulator, charges it up. There are important practical devices in which the electrical consequences of this are used. In *storage tubes*, a pattern of information in the form of fluctuations of electron beam current over a scan is transferred to the inner surface of a layer of insulator, which is equivalent to charging an array of condensers. The potential attained by an element of the surface will control the instantaneous beam current in a subsequent scan, and in this way the information 'written' on the screen can be 'read' as fluctuations in the beam current. Storage tubes are used for information storage in radar, and for similar applications in computers.

A further application is in television camera tubes. Basically, an optical image is transformed to a charge pattern by projection onto a photoemissive surface. The charge pattern is scanned by an electron beam. In some tubes the current that must flow to bring the image element to electrostatic equilibrium by secondary emission under a high (1500 volt) scanning beam provides the signal (*image iconoscope*; *scenioscope*). An alternative is to use a low energy (200 volt) electron beam and effectively measure the current supplied by the beam in making good the loss of photoelectrons during the remainder of the scanning cycle (*emitron*; *image orthicon*). In the *vidicon*, the latter principle is modified by the use of photoconductivity (Section 9.19) instead of photoemission.

5.13 **The double beam oscillograph.**   It is often convenient to display the time variations of two phenomena simultaneously on the screen of a cathode ray tube. This can be done in several ways.

(i) By using a cathode ray tube with two entirely separate gun structures in the same envelope. This is a good solution, but a costly one.

(ii) By using a single gun and deflector assembly, but switching the deflector voltage back and forth between two inputs. This demands electronic switching whose operation is rapid compared with the phenomena to be investigated, and is a severe limitation at high frequencies.

(iii) A beam from a single electron gun can be split, by using an additional plate midway between the deflectors so that the beam is physically split by it. This is simple and satisfactory, but has the disadvantage that it is difficult to eliminate interaction between the split beams and, more seriously, it is of course no longer possible to apply a balanced deflecting voltage to each beam, as discussed in Section 5.9, so that there will be some trapezium distortion.

5.14 **Damage to the screen.** If the electron beam is focused to a
fine spot and allowed to impinge for a long time on one region of the screen,
the crystal lattice of the phosphor is damaged by the sustained bombardment, and its luminous efficiency is reduced, so that part of a trace subsequently covering this region will appear dark by contrast with unaffected
regions. This effect, which is not reversible, is known as *screen burn*, and
with the high beam densities currently employed, it is possible to burn a
line trace, as well as a spot, in this way. Electron screen burn can be
avoided by care in operation, but a more serious difficulty is due to the
attachment of electrons to heavy residual atoms in the vacuum tube (the
vacuum, of course, can never be perfect, and a 'good' vacuum for this
purpose still contains 10^{16} molecules/m^3). These negative ions are much
more effective than electrons in causing damage to the phosphor, and
because of their greater mass, they are not appreciably deflected either
electrostatically or magnetically, so that they will always impinge near the
axis of the tube, where the phosphor will speedily deteriorate. This *ion
burn* is particularly serious in television picture tubes, as the picture is
spoilt in its region of maximum significance.

The problem may be simply dealt with by the so-called *ion trap*. The
electron gun is eccentrically mounted in the neck of the cathode ray tube,
so that both electrons and ions would miss the screen altogether, were
it not for a permanent magnet so placed as to deflect the electron beam
towards the screen. The ion beam is not affected, and impinges on the
wall of the tube where it can do no damage. The final (electrostatic)
focusing electrode of the gun may be obliquely terminated, with the
same effect.

5.15 **Magnetic focusing and deflection.** So far, only the electrostatic deflection and focusing of electron beams has been considered. It is
possible to produce the same effects magnetically, using for instance suitably designed coils. In principle, there is little to choose between the two
methods, and a choice can be made on the grounds of practical convenience.
Certainly, in considering, as we have done, the cathode ray tube as a
measuring instrument, electrostatic deflection is to be preferred, on
account of the intrinsically low impedance nature of deflecting coils, and
the difficulty of matching to them an amplifier of high impedance input.
In other applications, there are other factors to consider; for example
economic ones in the case of television receivers. The complex structure of
an electrostatically focused and deflected cathode ray tube is incompatible
with cheap quantity production, as the precision construction and alignment of lens components inside the vacuum tube itself is unavoidable,
while the whole device has a limited life determined by the cathode. The
cheapest cathode ray tube will be the one with least inside it, and it is

common practice to use both magnetic focusing and beam deflection (with external coils) in television picture tubes.

5.16 Electron lenses in general.

The lenses for an optical instrument are designed by painstaking computation or by graphical construction, in which the paths of sample rays are followed in detail. The elementary theory of thin lenses is insufficient for more than the crudest analysis, because its simplicity is the result of limiting attention to those rays which pass very close to the optical axis, and almost parallel to it, restrictions which are inadmissible in practice. The result is well known; when the restrictions are lifted, a point is no longer imaged as a point, and a number of separate defects, or aberrations, which contribute to this result, can be distinguished. It is possible to correct these aberrations, or at least to minimize their effects, by attention to the design of the optical system.

As would be expected, electron lenses show similar aberrations, and of these two are of major importance. The first of these is analogous to chromatic aberration in optics, and causes electrons of different energies to be brought to a focus at different points. This is an unavoidable consequence of electron optics. It is potentially serious because the electrons emitted from a thermionic cathode necessarily have a spread in velocities. The effect of this can be minimized by using the largest practicable accelerating voltage so that the energy spread of the electrons at the origin becomes insignificant. It also means that for good focus all lens potentials or currents must be well stabilized.

The second aberration of importance is spherical aberration, whereby rays entering a lens at different distances from the axis are brought to a focus at different points, so that even a point on the axis of the lens is not imaged as a point. It is a characteristic of all electron lenses of conventional design, electrostatic or magnetic, that they will exhibit spherical aberration, and it cannot be corrected by the combination of positive and negative elements, as in light optics (this is also true of the 'chromatic' aberration). It has been shown that lenses with axial electrodes, or lenses with an axial distribution of space charge, can be made free from spherical aberration, but so far it has not been possible to make a satisfactory lens of this type.

5.17 Resolving power of the electron lens—the electron microscope.

Leaving aside the question of aberrations, and supposing the perfect lens in this sense, what is the ultimate limit to its behaviour? The limit is set by the wave nature of light, for the diffraction resulting from this nature prevents the shadows thrown by an obstacle from being perfectly sharp. In particular, the image of a point will be a *diffraction pattern*, and not a point, and the ability of the lens to resolve the images of two points will depend on the degree of overlap of these patterns, whose size is determined by the wavelength of the light used. Hence the *resolving power* of any optical instrument will ultimately be limited by the wavelength of light. The resolving power is approximately one third the wavelength, so that the shortest visible wavelength (to which the eye is incidentally very insensitive) will give a resolving power of 1500 Å in a microscope objective of optimum design; points closer together than this will not be distinguished no matter how carefully the microscope is constructed.

This limitation is particularly irksome in microscopy, where one is usually anxious to push technique to its limits, and determined to extend these limits when they are reached. The resolving power of a lens sets limits which are not technical, but fundamental, and they can only be overcome by a radical transformation of approach, such as the use of 'light' of shorter wavelength. It is possible, though difficult, to use ultra-violet light in this way, but little can be done to extend the technique beyond, into the X-ray region, since there is nothing that could serve as an X-ray lens. If, as we have seen in Section 2.5, electrons have an associated de Broglie wavelength, then for electrons of 600 V energy, this is $\frac{1}{2}$ Å, and for 60 kV electrons it is $\frac{1}{30}$ Å, i.e. equivalent to X-ray wavelengths. If then the wave properties of the electron can be exploited, an electron microscope is in principle possible which will represent a great improvement over the best optical microscope. Now it is possible to make such a microscope in practice, using the electron lenses which have been described; this was done by Knoll and Ruska in 1931, using magnetic lenses.

A modern electron microscope using magnetic lenses is shown diagrammatically in Fig. 5.7. It is quite analogous to an optical microscope. The specimen is 'illuminated' by focusing an electron beam on it using a condensing lens. Electrons diverging from the object enter a converging lens (the objective) and the image thus produced is then further magnified by a second lens (the 'eyepiece'). The final image can be made visible by means of a fluorescent screen, or can be photographed directly, since photographic plates are sensitive to electrons as well as to light.

As with the optical microscope, a partially transparent object is necessary if a useful image is to be produced, and this means that only very thin objects can be examined. Even so, the energy lost by the electron beam in passing through is sufficient to heat the specimen locally, and unless it is a good thermal conductor, is likely to damage or destroy it (biological material is obviously particularly vulnerable in this respect). In these circumstances, useful information can often be derived from a 'replica' of refractory material which reproduces the topography of the object.

The resolving power of the electron microscope falls short of the theoretical ideal, since it is not possible to use high aperture electron lenses because of spherical aberration (Section 5.16). It is however possible to achieve resolving powers in the range 100 Å–25Å: this represents an advance of immense value, and brings biological entities like viruses and protein chains within the range of 'visibility'.

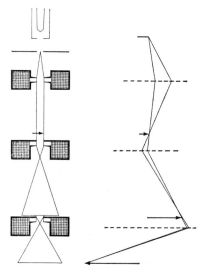

FIG. 5.7 (*Left*) Diagrammatic cross section of magnetic electron microscope. Each lens is a coil in a ferromagnetic case (shown heavily shaded). The external field is concentrated around the annular slot inside each coil, and provides the refracting element. The electron gun is at the top of the diagram, the object just above the second lens, and the final image at the bottom.

(*Right*) Schematic indication of the path of a single bundle of rays to indicate image formation in the electron microscope. (Adapted from Cosslett, V.E. *Electron Optics*, 2nd edn., The Clarendon Press, Oxford (1950).)

REFERENCES

1. PIERCE, J. R. *Theory and Design of Electron Beams*, Van Nostrand, Princeton (1954).

2. SPANGENBERG, K. R. *Vacuum Tubes*, McGraw-Hill, New York (1948).

3. SÜSSKIND, C. 'Electron guns and focusing for high-density electron beams', *Advances in Electronics and Electron Physics* **8**, 363 (1956).

4. COSSLETT, V. E. *Introduction to Electron Optics*, 2nd edn., Oxford University Press, Oxford (1950).

PROBLEMS

5.1 How many electrons per second are there in a beam of current 1 mA?

5.2 In Thomson's apparatus for the determination of e/m (see Chapter 1) the distance over which the magnetic and electrostatic deflecting fields are effective is 5 cm, and the fluorescent spot is 50 cm from the centre of this region. The beam is undeflected by the combined action of an electric field of 10^4volt/m and a magnetic field of $3\cdot2 \times 10^{-4}$weber/m². A deflection of 3° 6′ is produced by the magnetic field alone. Calculate from these data the value of e/m and the velocity of the electrons.

5.3 If the Thomson apparatus is modified so that the electric and magnetic fields are parallel and not perpendicular, the locus of the flurorescent spot produced by particles of various velocities is a parabola; give its equation.

5.4 An electron starts from rest at the negative plate of a parallel plate condenser to which a fixed potential difference of 500 V is applied. If the plate separation is 0·6 cm, after what time will the electron reach the positive plate?
Discuss the electron's motion if the applied potential is sinusoidal a.c. Consider the effect of the phase of the voltage with respect to the instant of release of the electron, and also the effect of the frequency.

5.5 A cathode ray tube has parallel deflecting plates 2·0 cm long and 0·5 cm apart. The vertical plates are 49 cm from the screen, and the horizontal plates 52 cm. What are the vertical and horizontal sensitivities if the accelerating voltage is (i) 1000 volts (ii) 1500 volts?

5.6 An electron with velocity v enters a region of uniform magnetic field whose direction is perpendicular to v. Show that the electron will move on a circular orbit, and calculate its radius and its angular velocity. How will the motion be affected if the field is not perpendicular to v?

5.7 The electrons of the first part of Question 5.4 are subjected to a magnetic field B parallel to the plates. What field strength will just prevent the electron from reaching the positive plate?
Taking the starting point of the electron as the origin of a coordinate system whose x-axis is along the electric, and z-axis along the magnetic, field, show that the position of the particle at a subsequent time t is given by

$$z = \frac{E}{B}(1 - \cos \omega t)$$

$$x = \frac{E}{B}(\omega t - \sin \omega t)$$

where $\omega = \frac{Be}{m}$

E is the electric field, B the magnetic field strength.

Chapter 6

The Control of Electron Current in a Vacuum— Space Charge and Velocity Modulation

6.1 The planar diode. This chapter will start from a consideration of a simple arrangement discussed in Section 4.10, in which a thermionic emitter and a collector electrode are contained *in vacuo*. To fix our ideas, we will suppose both electrodes to be plane and parallel. This arrangement is described as a *planar diode*.

If both electrodes are electrically isolated, equilibrium will be attained with the emitter at a small positive, the collector at a small negative potential with respect to earth. Between them will be a cloud of electrons— a space charge. The force on an electron throughout the space between the plates is directed toward the emitter, equilibrium signifying that a thermionically emitted electron will return to the emitter, like a projectile fired vertically from the earth's surface. If a battery is now connected between the emitter and collector so as to make the latter positive (so that we can now refer to the electrodes as cathode and anode respectively) a continuous current of electrons will flow, and if the potential difference is high enough, the current will correspond to the rate of thermionic emission from the cathode. In this case the force on an electron in the space between the electrodes will always be directed toward the anode.

6.2 Space-charge limited emission in the planar diode. We have now considered two extreme situations, and between them, for inter-mediate potential differences between the plates, the force on an electron will change in direction in between the cathode and the anode. Hence there must be a plane between the electrodes at which the force is zero. This plane we shall refer to as the *barrier*. Under these circumstances the electron current to the anode will be less than the thermionically determined saturation value, and will be *space-charge limited*. In calculating this current, we shall consider the force on a particular electron as it crosses the gap. There is no force on the electron at the barrier, so by Gauss's theorem the charge behind the barrier plane must be zero, and this is made up of the negative charge on those electrons which have left the cathode but not yet

reached the barrier, and a positive charge on the cathode itself. The electrons will cross the barrier with a finite but small velocity u_0, by virtue of
their finite velocity of emission from the cathode. In practice the electrons
will have a distribution of velocities, but we will disregard this at present.

Consider now an electron at point P, Fig. 6.1, which has left the barrier
B a distance x behind, *en route* for the anode A. It experiences a force due
to other charges in the neighbourhood, and these charges may be divided
into three categories.

(i) A negative charge due to the electrons in transit between the
barrier plane and P.

(ii) A negative charge due to the electrons in transit between P and the
anode.

(iii) A positive charge on the anode which must be equal to the sum of
(i) and (ii) by Gauss's theorem since there is no force on an electron at
the barrier.

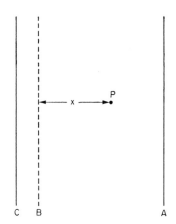

FIG. 6.1   Idealized planar diode. A—anode plane, B—barrier plane,
C—cathode plane.

Hence it follows that the electron at P only experiences a force due to the
electrons behind it—between the barrier and P.

How much charge is there between the barrier and P? Suppose the time
taken by the electron to cover the distance x between the barrier and P
was t. Then if the electron current density is $\mathcal{J}$, the charge between P and
the barrier is $\mathcal{J}t$ per unit area.

If F is the field at P, the equation of motion for an electron at P is

$$m \frac{d^2x}{dt^2} = eF = \frac{e}{\varepsilon_0} \mathcal{J}t,$$

$$\frac{d^2x}{dt^2} = \frac{e}{\varepsilon_0 m} \mathcal{J}t.$$

Integrating, we have

$$\frac{dx}{dt} = \frac{e}{2\varepsilon_0 m} \mathcal{J} t^2$$

(we are assuming that $\frac{dx}{dt} = 0$ at the barrier, i.e. u_0 is negligible).

Integrating a second time

$$x = \frac{e \, \mathcal{J} t^3}{6m\varepsilon_0}.$$

Now if the potential at P is V we can write

$$\tfrac{1}{2} m \left(\frac{dx}{dt}\right)^2 = eV.$$

Substituting for $\frac{dx}{dt}$ we can write

$$V = \frac{e \, \mathcal{J}^2 t^4}{8m\varepsilon_0{}^2},$$

and substituting for t in terms of x,

$$V = \frac{(6x)^{\frac{4}{3}}}{8} \left(\frac{\mathcal{J}}{\varepsilon_0}\right)^{\frac{2}{3}} \left(\frac{m}{e}\right)^{\frac{1}{3}}.$$

Writing this explicitly in terms of $\mathcal{J}$

$$\mathcal{J} = \frac{4}{9}\left(\frac{2e}{m}\right)^{\frac{1}{2}} \frac{\varepsilon_0 V^{3/2}}{x^2},$$

and since the current across each plane is the same,

$$\mathcal{J} = \frac{4}{9}\left(\frac{2e}{m}\right)^{\frac{1}{2}} \frac{\varepsilon_0 V_a{}^{3/2}}{d^2},$$

when V_a is the anode voltage, d the barrier-to-anode spacing.

This result for the space-charge limited current is known as the *Child-Langmuir equation*. The derivation above is strictly valid only if the electron velocity at the barrier is zero, and the result is useful only if the barrier is so close to the cathode that d may be taken as the interelectrode spacing. These assumptions are linked, and are both justified for applied voltages greater than a few tenths of a volt.

We can regard the anode voltage as determining the energy of each electron reaching it, but it determines the current flowing only indirectly, by altering the position of the barrier.

6.3 **Limitations of the treatment.** Our argument is oversimplified in two respects. First, we should recognize that the electron velocities at the barrier will be distributed. Allowance for this complicates the analysis very much, but does not alter the form of the current-voltage relationship. Secondly, the planar, one dimensional geometry of the problem is unrealistic, since most practical thermionic emitters are filamentary in form, with a coaxial cylinder as anode. Again, this only affects the Child-Langmuir equation by a change in numerical coefficient. In fact it can be shown that the three-halves power relationship is valid for all diodes, no matter what their geometry.

6.4 **The role of space charge in the diode.**   Most applications of the diode depend on the basic asymmetry of the tube—that one electrode is an electron emitter and the other is not. This is responsible for its ability to rectify an applied alternating voltage. The importance of the space-charge limitation of the current is less direct. If the current flowing is controlled by the distribution of charge in the interelectrode space, we might reasonably ask whether this current cannot be controlled by means of this charge. In fact this can be done, and the means of doing it were discovered, quite empirically, by de Forest in 1903, before the importance of space charge had been appreciated.

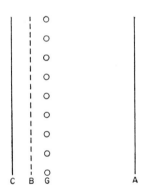

FIG. 6.2   Idealized planar triode. G—plane of grid wires.

6.5 **The triode.**   The procedure was to interpose a grid of fine wire between the anode and the cathode, so producing a three-electrode valve or *triode*, whereupon it was found that the anode current could be controlled by the potential of the grid, and in particular, cut off altogether by a sufficiently negative grid potential. By means of a load resistance in series with the anode, a fluctuating voltage applied to the grid could produce an amplified signal across the anode load.

Consider the arrangement of Fig. 6.2, again thinking in terms of the simplified planar arrangement. Suppose the grid G is given a negative charge. This charge will have little effect on the position of the barrier B (Section 6.2), and no significant effect on the force exerted on an electron between the barrier and the grid. This is because, as we saw in Section 6.2, the electron only experiences a force due to the space charge between it and the barrier plane. However, once an electron has passed the grid wires, it will experience a force, not only due to the electrons between it and the barrier, as in the diode, but also due to the negative charge on the grid wires.

The additional repulsion will give the electron more kinetic energy but the total kinetic energy must equal the electron potential energy at the anode, so the current will tend to fall; if it is to remain unchanged it will be necessary to increase the anode potential so that, for constant current, there is a relationship between anode voltage and the charge on the grid. Now the charge on the grid can be shown to be proportional to the grid voltage, and we obtain an expression of the form

$$I_a = f(V_a + \mu V_g),$$

where f is some function. This expression gives a relationship between the current flowing to the anode and the anode and grid voltages.

From a quantitative treatment it can be shown that

$$\mu = - \frac{2\pi d}{S \ln 2 \sinh\dfrac{\pi c}{S}},$$

where S is the distance between centres of grid wires, d is the grid-anode distance, and c the radius of grid wires, μ is known as the *amplification factor*.

The information embodied in the relation between I_a and V_a, V_g can be represented graphically in terms of the well-known *characteristics* of the triode (Fig. 6.3) and because of their usefulness, parameters other than μ are often specified, for instance the mutual conductance

$$g_m = \left(\frac{\partial I_a}{\partial V_g}\right)_{V_a},$$

and the anode slope resistance

$$\rho = - \left(\frac{\partial V_a}{\partial V_g}\right)_{I_a}.$$

Note: $\mu = g_m \rho.$

6.6 **Characteristics of this treatment.** The treatment of space charge that has been given here differs from that usually found in the

F

standard books. It is customary to calculate first the electrostatic field configuration in the absence of electrons, and calculate from that the trajectory of a single electron, as was done in the last chapter. Space charge effects are finally added as a perturbation, but since it is of the very essence of a valve that it operates by means of space charge it seems preferable to adopt an approach which recognizes the space charge from the beginning.

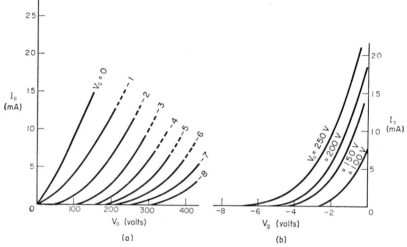

FIG. 6.3 Characteristic curves for a high impedance triode.
(a) Anode current—anode voltage characteristics.
(b) Anode current—grid voltage characteristics.

6.7 **Grid-anode capacitance.** The density of electrons in the grid-anode space is, however, quite low and can be neglected compared with the charges on the anode and grid themselves. For this reason, we can ignore the electrons and calculate the electrostatic capacitance between these two electrodes. The magnitude of this capacitance is $\sim \frac{1}{2}$pF.

6.8 **Applications of the triode.** The application of the valve in oscillator and amplifier circuits follows directly from $I_a = f(V_a + \mu V_g)$; the associated circuits are outside our scope, but there is one item of physics involved which calls for comment—in the applications we are converting energy into a chosen form. The source of the energy is the H.T. supply to the valve, and the transformation takes place as follows. A fluctuating grid voltage leads to fluctuations in the anode current. With a resistive load in the anode circuit the anode potential will change, assuming constant H.T. voltage, and the change will be in such a direction that the anode potential decreases while the anode current increases, and vice versa. Hence, by comparison with the situation in the absence of the signal on the grid, more current will reach the anode when the potential is lower, and less when the anode potential is higher than average. Because of this, less energy will be dissipated as heat at the anode, and the difference will be available in the anode load, where some of it can be usefully employed. The extreme case of this energy transfer is the Class C operation of a valve, where a tuned circuit is energized by a burst of current once per cycle. The transfer is only efficient if the anode voltage and current are approximately 90° out of phase.

6.9 **Limitations of the triode.** The points that have been raised cover the basic physics of the triode—a matter of the collective interactions of electrons, considered of course as classical charged particles. The practical limitations of the triode also depend on the physical principles of its operation. They are connected with the low value of the slope resistance and the excessive grid-anode capacitance. The latter provides feedback between grid and anode circuits which can lead to oscillation.

6.10 **The tetrode.** Both these effects can be overcome by placing a second wire grid in the tube, quite close to the anode, and connecting it to a separate H.T. supply. It acts as an electrostatic screen between grid and anode, reducing the grid-anode capacitance, and increasing the slope resistance. Typical characteristics of this valve, the *tetrode*, are given in Fig. 6.4. They show the expected features, but are disappointing because of the dip in the I_a, V_a curve and the corresponding rise in the screen current I_s. This is due to electrons striking the anode and causing secondary emission. When this occurs in a triode the secondaries will be unable to escape, but in the tetrode they can be collected by the screen if its potential is favourable, and it is this effect which is responsible for the 'negative resistance' region on the characteristic. This has been exploited for

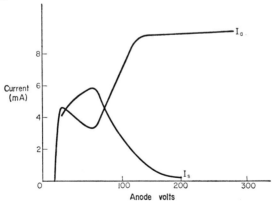

FIG. 6.4   Plot of anode and screen current against anode voltage for tetrode. Control grid potential held at 0 V, screen grid potential held at 100 V.

certain purposes, but for normal applications it is a source of unwanted instability and the 'safe' working range of the tetrode is too small to be of much value.

6.11   **The pentode.**   The situation can be radically improved by the addition of yet another grid (the suppressor) between the screen and the anode, to prevent loss of secondaries from the anode. This grid is usually connected to the cathode, and repels the secondaries to the anode once again. The I_a, V_a characteristics of the pentode valve are shown in Fig. 6.5. They are seen to have the features sought, without the obnoxious effects of secondary emission.

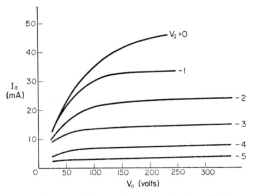

FIG. 6.5 I_a, V_a characteristics of a pentode for different values of V_g the control grid potential. The potential of the screen grid is held at 250 V, and the suppressor at 0 V.

6.12   **The variable-mu pentode.**   It was indicated in Section 6.5 that the amplification factor μ of a valve is controlled by the spacing of the grid wires, and the distance from the cathode. For instance, a pentode will have a low cut-off if the grid wires are close together and near to the cathode, but a more open construction will give rise to a higher cut-off. (A triode or pentode is said to cut off when the negative bias on the grid is just sufficient to prevent electrons reaching the anode).

The grid-wire spacing can deliberately be made non-uniform by winding a helical grid of unequal pitch around the cathode. This means that the amplification factor for different parts of the valve is different, and a pentode with this type of grid will have its $I_a - V_g$ characteristic modified as shown in the diagram (Fig. 6.6). This is called a variable-mu pentode, and it is useful in automatic gain control circuits.

6.13   **The beam power tetrode.**   In those cases where a valve is required to deliver a significant power so that the anode current is correspondingly high, a modified tetrode can be employed—the *beam power tetrode*—in which secondary emission current from the anode can be prevented without a suppressor grid.

The screen grid is placed further from the anode than is usual in the tetrode, and the grid wires are aligned with those of the control grid. This tends to focus the electron stream in a well-defined beam, a process which is accentuated by two *beam-forming electrodes* connected to the cathode. The result of the concentration of the current is to establish a substantial space charge in the screen-anode space, and this can be sufficient to repel secondary electrons emitted from the anode. Those emitted tangentially could still reach the screen but they are repelled back by the beam-forming electrodes. As would be anticipated, the mechanism ceases to be effective at low anode currents (below 40 mA in a typical case) so that the beam tetrode can only take the place of the pentode in output stages.

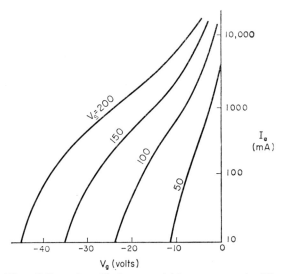

FIG. 6.6   Plot of I_a against V_g for a variable-mu pentode. The family of curves represents different values of the screen grid potential, V_s. V_a is constant at 150 V.

6.14   **The behaviour of space-charge controlled valves at high frequencies.**   The ultimate limitations on the performance of space-charge controlled valves are most clearly brought out when the attempt is made to use them as amplifiers and oscillators at high frequencies. As the frequency is raised, the following effects become important.

First, the grid-anode capacity of the triode lowers the input impedance. This can be avoided by using a pentode as already discussed.

The input impedance of a pentode is in turn lowered by the combination of the grid-cathode capitance and the inductance of the cathode lead. These can be reduced by making the cathode area as small as possible, and by shortening the cathode lead. The cathode lead can be minimized by using a pressed glass base rather than the traditional pinch seal with a separate base and pins.

The ultimate restriction is the finite time that the electron necessarily takes to travel from cathode to grid—the transit time ($\sim 10^{-9}$ sec). In passing the grid, each electron induces a transient charge, and hence a current, on the grid, and this can be shown to be equivalent to a further reduction of the input impedance.

Valves can be designed to minimize these drawbacks. Thus a triode oscillator can be used up to 3000 Mc/s if the transit time is made small by using a planar construction with a very small grid-cathode clearance, if the grid is connected to earth to prevent capacitative coupling between input and output, and if the grid itself is part of a disc which is brought out of the envelope as a glass-metal seal, so that grid leads are avoided altogether. This arrangement, used with coaxial line tuned circuits, represents the ultimate performance of which the space-charge controlled valve is capable. To go further we must adopt a new principle. This is done in *velocity modulation* in which the transit time phenomenon which necessarily limits the performance of space-charge limited devices, is turned to good account.

6.15 Velocity modulated electron devices—the klystron.

Electrons are formed into a beam by a gun similar to that described in Section 5.6. They pass through an input tuned circuit which at the frequencies we are concerned with is a resonant cavity, cylindrical in shape and symmetrical about the axis, similar to the one shown in cross section in Fig. 6.7. The electrons enter and leave the cavity through grids, and experience forces due to any radio-frequency fields between the grids.

Leaving the cavity, the electrons enter a space free from radio-frequency fields, where each electron can move with the velocity it acquired in the cavity. The value of this velocity will depend on the time of the electron's passage in relation to the phase of the radio-frequency voltage on the cavity. Fig. 6.8 shows that the 'velocity modulation' will cause the electrons to 'bunch' because the faster ones will catch up with the slower.

If the bunched beam now enters a second cavity, tuned to the same frequency as the first, the passage of a bunch will induce a movement of charge on the cavity, and a corresponding potential difference between the opposite grids. If the electron beam is out of phase with the fluctuating potential difference, then energy will be transferred from the beam to the cavity; if it is in phase, the cavity will lose energy. Hence under suitable conditions, energy can be drawn from the accelerator voltage via the

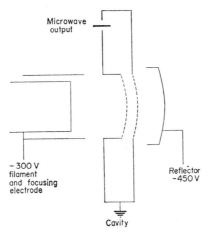

FIG. 6.7   Cross section of reflex klystron, showing potentials of the electrodes. (From Thomson J. and Callick E.B. *Electron Physics and Technology*, English Universities Press, London (1959).)

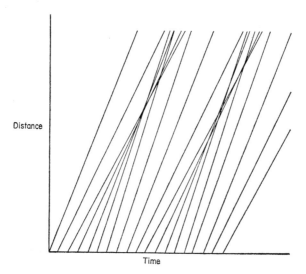

FIG. 6.8   The family of lines is a plot of position on axis against time for a series of electrons leaving the cathode of a klystron at equal intervals of time and being accelerated or retarded by the field of the cavity, assumed sinusoidal. The 'bunching' effect of the field is clearly shown.

electron beam, and transformed into radio frequency in the form of an amplified output from the second cavity. The electron beam circuit is terminated by an anode.

The drawback of the device we have described as an amplifier is the inherently high Q of the resonant cavities. For this reason the klystron is only useful as an oscillator, where this feature is an advantage. Some measure of tuning of the cavity can be effected by changing its shape, but it is not feasible to tune the two cavities simultaneously in this way. This problem can be solved if only a single cavity is used, and the electron beam is reflected back into it from an electrode which is held at a negative potential with respect to the cathode—this is the *reflex klystron* (Fig. 6.7). It is not often employed as a power source at microwave frequencies, but is a convenient local oscillator for the superheterodyne reception of microwave signals. It can be used to wavelengths as small as $\frac{1}{2}$ cm, the limit being set by the decreasing size of the cavity. This leads to a decreased impedance, and means that a higher beam current is necessary to excite it. It is difficult to produce a beam that will do this without space-charge repulsion making it too large to pass through the apertures in the cavity.

6.16   **The travelling-wave tube.**   In a klystron the electron beam interacts with a radio-frequency field whilst crossing the cavity. It is possible to construct a device—*a travelling-wave tube*—in which the interaction can be increased by the use of multiple cavities. The array of cavities used will function as a delay line, and what really happens is that the propagation of an electromagnetic wave along the line takes place sufficiently slowly to be in synchronism with the velocities of the electrons in the beam. A flow of energy can then take place from the beam to the wave which involves the ultimate amplification of the wave as it travels towards the output end of the line.

The simplest kind of transmission line is a single wire, and the velocity of propagation along it is approximately c, the velocity of electromagnetic waves in free space. If the wire be coiled into a helix of mean diameter d and with t turns per unit length, the velocity of wave propagation along the axis of the helix will be $c/\pi td$. In this way the velocity can be reduced to say, $c/10$, approximately equal to that of a beam of electrons of $2\cdot5$ kV energy. All that is required is an electron gun to form the beam and direct it along the axis of the helix, and a longitudinal magnetic field to prevent it from spreading. The input signal is fed to the gun end of the line via a waveguide transformer, and the output drawn off from the other end in a similar manner. A great advantage of the device is that the helix is not a resonant structure so that amplification over a wide frequency band is possible.

Mathematical analysis of the interaction between the electron beam and an electromagnetic wave show that four wave modes will result. Two of these are irrelevant to our purpose, one is the slow wave we have mentioned, and the fourth—the 'backward wave'—has a negative group velocity. The latter provides feedback and makes for instability in a travelling-wave tube which is intended as an amplifier, so that the walls of the tube are usually made conducting in a region near the midpoint to attenuate it.

Alternatively, with a different 'slow wave' structure in the form of a parallel line with interpenetrating fingers, the latter slotted to admit the electron beam, the beam can be made to interact with the backward wave instead (the input and output are now of course reversed). It is possible to make an oscillator on this principle, and since the slow wave structure used is dispersive (the velocity of a wave on it depends on frequency) tuning over an octave is possible simply by varying the beam accelerator voltage to bring the beam velocity to match the appropriate wave.

Travelling-wave tubes of many different types have been developed but the examples mentioned will suffice to illustrate the principles. The wideband or tunable characteristics of the travelling wave tube are an attractive feature, but its size, and the bulk of the magnet required to produce the longitudinal field are major drawbacks. Travelling-wave amplifiers are used in the output stages of relay stations in microwave communication links, but for the amplification of threshold signals, in radar or satellite communication for instance, the noise of the travelling-wave tube (Section 15.1) is a prohibitive disadvantage, and the maser (Section 15.8) is to be preferred.

6.17 **The magnetron.** This tube was specifically developed to produce a very powerful pulse of microwave radiation, and for this purpose it is unsurpassed. It can also function as a source of continuous microwaves, but the efficiency is not so high.

Basically, the structure is a concentric diode, but with an anode incorporating an even number (usually eight) of resonant cavities (Fig. 6.9). The cathode is an oxide cathode of large radius, and the valve operates in a uniform magnetic field of flux density $\sim \frac{1}{10}$ weber/m^2 parallel to the axis.

Consider the operation of the valve as a diode. Electrons travel on a radial path between cathode and anode in the absence of the magnetic field. If the magnetic field be imagined to increase from zero, the electrons will be appreciably deflected, and there will be a certain field (cut-off) at which the electrons will not reach the anode at all. Similar circumstances will apply when space-charge limited conditions occur. Some of the space charge consists of electrons leaving the cathode, and returning to it, and some perhaps consists of electrons orbiting continually in interelectrode space.

The tangential motion of the electrons is introduced by the magnetic field, and it is this which interacts with the resonant cavities. The latter will resonate together as a coupled system. Suppose the field across one cavity (A in Fig. 6.9), is such as to accelerate one electron which passes close to it near the extremity of its trajectory. If it passes the next cavity (B) and is again accelerated, then energy will be abstracted from the electromagnetic field, the electron will move closer to the cathode and will eventually return to it giving back its energy as heat. If, on the other hand, the electron reaches B when the electromagnetic field is out of phase, energy will be transferred to the field from the electron, and as a result the electron will move onto a larger orbit, eventually reaching the anode. The result of the energy transfer is to sustain oscillation in the cavities.

Oscillation such as we have described, with A and B out of phase, is the so-called π mode. Other more complex modes are possible, but the π mode can be stabilized by connecting together appropriate points on the segments between the cavities, a procedure known as 'strapping'.

A proper theory of the magnetron is a problem of the utmost difficulty; what has been said can give no more than a crude idea of its operation.

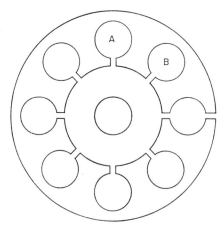

FIG. 6.9   Cross section of a magnetron, showing central cathode and the anode resonator structure. The magnetic field is directed perpendicular to the plane of the diagram. Microwave power is withdrawn by way of the coupling hole at the right.

6.18   **Summary of chapter.**   We have now discussed the main ways in which electron motion in a vacuum can be controlled to meet practical needs, either with respect to trajectory (electron optics), or with respect to the current carried, by space-charge repulsion or velocity modulation. (Some of the devices considered here employ more than one of these principles.)

We must now consider the behaviour of electrons in interaction with matter. Fundamentally the problems to be encountered are more complicated, but it is possible to simplify them into the kind of terms with which we have already become familiar, and it is from this simplification that practical applications are possible.

References

1. MOULLIN, E. B. 'The amplification factor of the triode', *Proc. I.E.E.* **104** C, 222 (1957).

2. SPANGENBERG, K. R. *Vacuum Tubes*, McGraw-Hill, New York (1948).

Problems

6.1 The potential minimum in a planar diode operating under space-charge limited conditions is $-V_m$ volts. Show that $V_m = -(kT/e) \ln P$ where P is the probability that an electron will have sufficient energy to pass the potential minimum.

6.2 A planar diode has electrodes in the form of discs 0·8 cm in diameter. What must be the value of the interelectrode spacing if the voltage drop is to be 100 V at 100 mA?

6.3 Calculate the electron transit time, in the diode of the previous question.

6.4 In the same diode, the cathode has a work function of 1·8 V, and the constant A in the thermionic emission equation (Section 4.9) is 10^4 amp/m². It operates at a temperature of 1600°K. What will be the observed current at 100 V applied if the separation is halved?

6.5 A cavity magnetron has an anode block of 2 cm internal diameter, and a cathode of 1·3 cm diameter. Find an approximate value of the magnetic field required to cut off the anode current at an anode voltage of 15 kV. (Hint: Neglect space charge and the curvature of anode and cathode.)

Chapter 7

Electrical Conduction in Gases

7.1 Historical. In the eighteenth century, when the experimental investigation of electricity was begun, the subject-matter was what we should now call electrostatics—the investigation of small quantities of charge, at a high electric potential. In the use of such crude measuring instruments as electroscopes, attention was naturally focused on the problem of leakage currents. In this connection it was commonly assumed that air, and other gases, were perfect electrical insulators, but later experiments showed this to be erroneous, and that small currents could flow through a gas. Furthermore, under suitable conditions, the electrical state of the gas could be abruptly changed, leading to spectacular phenomena like the electric spark and arc. The electrical properties of gases at low pressures revealed altogether different phenomena, strikingly beautiful and with an aura of mystery that invited closer study.

7.2 The gaseous plasma. A common feature of the state of a gas when conducting electricity is the emission of light, and the region of the gas emitting light is known as a *plasma*. Macroscopically it is electrically neutral, but on the microscopic scale, no matter how it is produced, it contains electrons (more rarely negative ions) and positive ions as well as neutral gas molecules. The electrons and positive ions result from the ionization of a proportion of the gas molecules, to an extent which depends on the origin of the plasma, and the circumstances of its continued existence. At low pressures the proportion of ionized atoms may approach 100%; it is usually much lower. Very densely ionized plasmas will be discussed in the next chapter.

7.3 The key problem—the origin of the gaseous ions. Notice that the thermal kinetic energy of the gas at room temperature is totally inadequate to produce appreciable ionization. Take for instance the vapour of the alkali metal caesium, an atom with the lowest known ionization potential, 3·89 eV. The chance of a single atom acquiring by a collision the energy required to ionize it, is only 1 in 10^{60} at room temperature, and even at the temperature of a flame ($\sim 1800°C$ for a bunsen flame) the proportion of ionized atoms is still small, though sufficient in this case to give the flame an appreciable electrical conductivity. Hence the ionization necessary to make a gas conducting is not normally there already; it has to be produced, and the question naturally arises, how does this occur?

7.4 **The gas diode.** We can see the answer to this if we consider a thermionic diode of the type discussed in Section 6.2. We will suppose that it operates initially in a high vacuum under space-charge limited conditions, but that a small trace of gas is subsequently introduced. At a low applied voltage, the presence of the gas makes little difference. It does make *some* difference, because the character of the electron motion on which the space charge limited condition depends is altered by the gas, since electrons are no longer freely accelerated by a field, but lose energy in collision with gas molecules, and attain a uniform average velocity.

If the voltage is increased, there will come a point at which the gas makes a major difference—the current passed suddenly increases above the space-charge limited value so that unless it is limited by the external circuit, it will proceed to the destruction of the tube. The reason for this behaviour is that, at the voltage applied, an electron can gain energy from the field between collisions in excess of the ionization potential of the gas molecules. In an ensuing collision, it is possible for the electron to transfer the energy to a molecule and ionize it. The electron so produced, like the primary, is swept away by the field, but by comparison the heavy positive ion is slow-moving and so remains behind, and serves to neutralize the electron space charge, so giving rise to a thermionic current greater than the vacuum value. The interelectrode space is then occupied by a gaseous plasma.

7.5 **Energy balance in a plasma.** This simple example illustrates the way in which any plasma is produced and maintained. Initially, electrons are accelerated in an electric field until they are able to ionize the gas molecules by collision, and the field then adjusts itself so that equilibrium is just maintained, that is to say that the depletion of the plasma is made good by further ionization. The ionization requires the expenditure of energy by the external circuit, and the two factors—ionization (charge balance) and energy balance—determine the equilibrium conditions in the plasma.

Taking a small volume element in the plasma, the loss of ionization must be by recombination of the electrons and the positive ions, or by the egress of ions and electrons. Now, in the conditions of the plasma, recombination can be shown to be unimportant, so any loss of ionization must be due to the latter alternative. The departure of ions and electrons in this way requires the existence of outwardly directed electric fields, and a considerable concentration gradient. This requires that the plasma be limited in extent in space. The plasma in a spark or arc has well-defined boundaries in the absence of any physical constraint on its size, but in other discharge phenomena at low pressures the boundary is often the wall of the containing vessel. In either case, recombination of ions and electrons can take place at the surface of the plasma, and this is the chief means by which ions are removed from the plasma. The corresponding source of ionization is electron impact, as we have seen.

The ionization energy transferred from the primary electron to the ion is released on recombination, and dissipated as kinetic energy (heat). The plasma also loses energy by collisions occurring with electrons which are not sufficiently energetic to ionize the molecule, but which instead raise it to an excited state, the energy so transferred being lost when the molecule returns to the ground state with the emission of a photon. This is the source of the light mentioned in Section 7.2.

Because energy is dissipated at the surface of a plasma, but generated throughout its volume, the form of the plasma will normally be one with a high volume/surface ratio, very often a cylinder with its axis along the direction of current flow. Also, the current density is the quantity of primary importance, and the role of voltage drop in gaseous conduction is largely subordinate, and determined by the particular process which has established the plasma. Clearly the plasma cannot occupy all the space between the electrodes, since there must always be a region where electrons can gain sufficient energy to maintain ionization before entering the plasma.

7.6 Ion and electron temperatures in a plasma.

From what has been said it will be clear that a gaseous plasma is not in thermal equilibrium, and that it is maintained by the transfer of energy from an electric field by means of electrons. This requires that although the electrons, neutral gas atoms, and positive ions occupy the space of the plasma in a homogeneous mixture, the energy is not uniformly divided amongst them. In other words, although each species is in thermal equilibrium within itself, the corresponding temperatures differ in the three cases. The energy of the electrons is always very high, the kinetic energy corresponding to a temperature of $\sim 10,000°K$ for instance in the positive column of a glow discharge. The energy of the neutral molecules is quite low, perhaps only a few degrees above the temperature of the environment. Depending on circumstances, the positive ion temperature may be close to that of the neutral molecules, or it may be higher (up to $1000°K$) depending on pressure. The coexistence of the electrons, atoms and ions at different temperatures is due to inefficient heat transfer. Because the electron is so much lighter than the positive ion ($1/1850$ at least), the amount of kinetic energy which an electron can lose in an *elastic* collision with a gas molecule is small, and such collisions are the most frequent, and the usual means of bringing about thermal equilibrium in a gas mixture. If the electron can gain energy from the field more rapidly than it can lose it by elastic collision, the electron temperature will be raised above that of the unionized gas as in the cases we are considering.

7.7 **The thyratron.** For an example of the practical importance of the properties of a gaseous plasma, we will return to space-charge limited emission in a vacuum, this time in the triode. Imagine the addition of a small concentration of gas, say mercury vapour to a pressure of $0\cdot01$ mmHg. In the absence of the gas, electrons will reach the anode only when the grid potential is below cut-off. If the valve is cut off the presence of the gas will not significantly change this state of affairs.

If gas is present, and the grid is driven momentarily positive to a sufficient extent, ionization of the gas in the grid-cathode space can occur, the space charge is now neutralized by the plasma, and the cathode is screened from the grid by it, so that the grid is now quite ineffective. A large current will now flow to the anode, almost entirely independent of what potential is applied to the grid. So the gas-filled triode is no longer a device in which the grid can exert a continuous control over the anode current, but is more like a switch, triggered by the application of a positive pulse to the grid, which can be switched off only when the anode voltage drops to zero.

The value of a switch is largely determined by its speed of operation. The speed of switching in the thyratron is the speed at which a plasma can be established filling the space between the electrodes; this depends on the grid voltage, but is usually in the range 10^{-7}–10^{-5} sec. The discharge is switched off by putting the anode volts to zero, but the plasma does not vanish instantaneously, and if the anode voltage is restored before the expiry of the *recovery time*, conduction can be resumed independent of the grid potential. A typical value of the recovery time is 10^{-3} sec. This value is determined by recombination and diffusion in the tube. It can be reduced considerably by special tube design, and is shorter ($\sim 10^{-8}$ sec) for the hydrogen thyratron.

Thyratrons are often used for the controlled switching of large currents in pulsing circuits, for instance in radar and for spot welding, and also in the control of a.c. machinery, by switching on for only a controlled part of a half-cycle. The switch will be reset at the end of the half-cycle, since the alternating supply necessarily takes the anode voltage through zero.

In addition to the recovery or de-ionization time, important quantities in thyratron operation are the maximum current rating, which is ultimately limited by heating of the anode, and by the capacity of the cathode to withstand positive ion bombardment without deterioration. Secondly, the voltage that can be applied to the anode without bringing about conduction in the gas irrespective of the grid potential is important, and this is determined by the position of the grid with respect to the cathode.

The gas used in most small thyratrons is mercury vapour, the required pressure being maintained by a droplet of the liquid metal in the envelope. If a gas like hydrogen were used, the gas pressure would decrease with time on account of 'clean-up', whereby some of the gas molecules become adsorbed on the electrodes, until eventually there are too few gas molecules present to provide a plasma. In the case of mercury, the drop of liquid provides a reservoir to provide for this contingency, but since the vapour pressure of the mercury varies exponentially with temperature, the latter must be controlled fairly closely if the pressure inside the tube is to be kept within working limits. This is important for heavy duty thyratrons. In fact it is common practice to use hydrogen in this case, where the high breakdown voltage of this gas provides a high 'hold-off' voltage.

The voltage drop across a conducting thyratron is usually about 8–20 volts. The plasma is approximately at anode potential, and most of the voltage drop thus occurs at the cathode. This is just sufficient to accelerate an electron leaving the cathode to the velocity necessary for ion production. A discharge in which the *cathode fall* is of the same order as the ionization potential of the gas (the ionization potential of mercury is $10\cdot44$ V) is called an *arc*.

7.8   **The Townsend discharge.**   To study the fundamental processes by which a gas is made conducting, we will turn to another example—a simple planar diode with a photosensitive cathode, the latter being irradiated so that a small photocurrent flows. In the absence of gas, this current may be about 10^{-10} amp which is far too small for space charge effects to be at all important, so the current to the anode should be independent of anode voltage provided the latter is positive.

If now a gas is introduced into the tube, at low voltages the photocurrent is unchanged, but at high voltages it begins to grow. This growth takes place when an electron leaving the cathode is accelerated by the field until it has enough energy to make an inelastic ionizing collision with a gas molecule. In this process a second electron is produced, which is itself accelerated so that it too will be able to produce an ion-electron pair. In this way, a cascade of electrons can be built up for each single primary, and it is these electrons which form the enhanced current. (It is of course necessary that the current across any plane in the gas should be constant, and although this condition appears to be violated, in fact the principle is safeguarded by the motion of the positive ions produced towards the cathode.) This gas multiplication is used in many single stage photocells to provide amplification of the signal, but the amount of amplification permitted is limited by the susceptibility of the cathode to damage from positive ion bombardment.

7.9 Calculation of the current in a Townsend avalanche. Let us now investigate this *Townsend electron avalanche* in more detail. Suppose that an electron can create a new electrons per unit length of its path in the field direction. n such electrons will produce dn new electrons in a distance dx where

$$dn = andx$$

or
$$n = n_0 \exp (ax),$$

where n_0 is the electron concentration at the cathode. This may also be written in terms of the current

$$i = i_0 \exp (ax).$$

Imagine an electron starting from the cathode at zero energy and being accelerated by the field. If the collision mean free path of the gas is longer than the distance to the anode, the probability of ionization is small. If on the other hand, the collision mean free path is short, the electron will not have the opportunity of gaining energy sufficient to bring about ionization—the energy will be too readily dissipated in elastic or exciting collisions. At intermediate values of mean free path, ionization will be relatively more probable, and the multiplication process described will be favoured. The crucial factor here is the *energy acquired by the electron between collisions*. This is proportional to the field E, and to the mean free path. The mean free path of a gas is inversely proportional to pressure (Section 3.9) so that, if we have two different instances of multiplication, it will be possible to compare them at corresponding values of the parameter (E/p).

7.10 The self-sustaining discharge. In these conditions, if the illumination of the cathode which produces the primary current is interrupted, the avalanche will vanish as the last electron is swept to the anode. If the voltage across the tube is increased, a point is reached when the current through the tube is *not* interrupted in this way—the current is self-sustaining and referred to as a *Townsend discharge* after its first investigator. If the current is to be self-sustaining, electrons must be emitted from the cathode, and these must arise from the flow of current itself. Important factors here are the photoelectric emission by the light produced by molecular excitation in the discharge, the release of electrons from the cathode by ion bombardment, or by the impact of atoms in metastable excited states (those excited states where the return transition is 'forbidden' by

G

spectroscopic selection rules, so that the lifetime of the excited state will be long enough to give it a significant chance of diffusing to the cathode while excited). It should be noted that positive ions themselves cannot gain enough energy from the field to ionize molecules in the gas.

Suppose the electron emission from the cathode is now n_0' instead of n_0 as in Section 7.9.

Then $n_0'(e^{ad} - 1)$ extra electrons will be produced, where d is the inter-electrode gap; this number of positive ions will be produced. The number of secondary electrons, no matter what the mechanism of their production, will be proportional to this number, and if we call the constant of proportionality γ, then

$$n_0' = n_0 + \gamma n_0' (e^{ad} - 1),$$

$$\frac{n_0'}{n_0} = \{1 - \gamma (e^{ad} - 1)\}^{-1};$$

or, in terms of current flowing, working with rates of production of electrons, and remembering that the current at the cathode is the *difference* of the electron and ion flows,

$$i = i_0 \frac{e^{ad}}{1 - \gamma (e^{ad} - 1)}.$$

7.11 Paschen's law.   Now if $\gamma (e^{ad} - 1) = 1$, the current becomes infinite. In reality the current will remain finite, but the assumptions on which our analysis is based will cease to be valid. For instance we have ignored the distortion of the field due to space charge, so that the argument necessarily applies only to very small currents. It is none the less clear that the condition above represents a significant discontinuity in the behaviour of the gas, which is known as the *sparking potential*. At higher voltages we will have created a gaseous plasma—something which is absent from the Townsend discharge.

It might be anticipated that the sparking potential would be indefinitely reduced if the separation of the electrodes in the gas is reduced, but a consideration of the argument of Section 7.9 shows that it is not so, and that the sparking potential goes through a minimum value at a certain critical distance.

For a given gas the sparking potential depends on the pressure P of the gas and the electrode separation only through the product Pd. This is a statement of *Paschen's law*. It follows from the argument in Section 7.9 that the number of ions produced by an electron in traversing the gap depends on the number of collisions (proportional to Pd) and the energy gained in a

mean free path, $E\lambda$. Now $\lambda \propto 1/P$, and $E = V/d$; so $ad = Pd \, F \left(\dfrac{V}{Pd} \right)$,

where F is some function.

In general the dependence of V on Pd passes through a minimum, increasing rapidly at lower values of Pd (because of the small number of molecules at low pressure) and more slowly at higher values. An immediate consequence of this is the observation that, for voltages below a certain minimum, no discharges will occur. At atmospheric pressure this amounts to some 300 volts.

It is important in high voltage technology that sparking potentials should be as high as possible. One way of achieving this is to choose a gas with an abnormally small electron mean free path. A gas with this property will be one where electrons tend to be captured by neutral molecules to give a stable negative ion, so that the electrons are removed before they attain enough energy to form positive ions and further electrons by collision. Gases which behave in this way are said to be *electronegative*. The halogens and their compounds are conspicuous examples of this behaviour.

7.12 **The spark discharge.** If a voltage substantially higher than the sparking potential is suddenly applied to a gas, or if the pressure is high, the ionization density associated with the electron avalanche is very great, and a heavy current can flow. The capacity of the external circuit is usually limited, so that the current flowing will be transient—a *spark*. In the short time involved, the positive ions will make little contribution to the current, but their space charge as the electrons are swept through will set up a lateral field which will draw in photoelectrons produced in the surrounding gas, and in this way will establish a conducting channel. The lightning stroke originates in this way, the conducting path being set up in stages, and when it is complete, a current of up to 10,000 amp of a millisecond duration will flow from the earth to the cloud.

A conducting channel of this kind is referred to as a *streamer* and streamer mechanisms are important in the many cases of electric breakdown in a gas where time does not permit the build-up of a Townsend avalanche (Section 7.14). The streamers are probably formed by the *photoionization* of atoms by the absorption of radiation emitted in a region where ionization by collision is occurring, so that the ionized region, once initiated, can extend rapidly into a streamer.

7.13 **The corona discharge.** In avalanche formation, there are circumstances when the geometry of the electrodes is such that the establishment of an avalanche in part of the interelectrode region causes the field in the remaining region to decrease, so that a spark will not be established. The individual avalanches will have the appearance of transient, light-emitting threads, and their aggregate makes up the *corona*.

7.14 **Time lags in discharges.** Returning to the Townsend discharge, experiment shows that it can be initiated at the sparking potential even if no provision is made for photoemission from the cathode. In this case the electrons which intitiate the avalanche are due to cosmic radiation, background radioactivity of the apparatus or its surroundings, or similar chance cause. This introduces a *time lag* before the occurrence of break-down which will, in the nature of things, show wide statistical variation. This will generally mask the more definite *formative* time lag of the *discharge*, which in the case we have considered would be shortest for the photoelectric process of electron regeneration (10^{-10} sec), and longest (10^{-3} sec) for the diffusion of metastables to the cathode, with the positive ion mechanism between.

It is possible for the discharge to be not completely self-sustaining, but to die away after a time interval, giving a sizeable burst of current initiated by a single electron in the discharge. This is the basis of operation of the *Geiger-Müller counter*, where the primary electrons are produced by the high energy radiation to be studied, and the discharge is 'quenched' de-liberately so as to be non-self-sustaining.

7.15 The effect of space charge on the Townsend discharge.
For a low-pressure gas, the Townsend theory provides an adequate picture of a self-sustaining discharge up to currents of the order of microamps. For higher currents, the distortion of the field by space charge begins to be important, and it arises in the following way. The current crossing any plane in the gas must be the same. At a plane near the anode, there are many electrons in transit, but at a plane near the cathode, hardly any. The

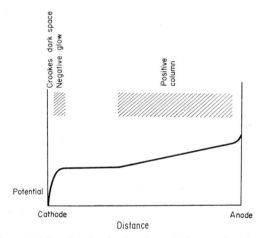

FIG. 7.1   Potential distribution in the glow discharge, showing the cathode fall in potential. The shaded areas show the principal regions of light emission in the discharge.

current in the latter case must be made up by an increased contribution of positive ions. Since the latter are slow-moving by comparison with the electrons, the same current can only be carried by a higher concentration of the ions, so that the region near the cathode will contain a preponderance of positive ions, and the associated space charge will distort the field. In fact the field distribution in the tube will be as shown in Fig. 7.1, where practically all the voltage is dropped near the cathode—the so-called *cathode fall* in potential.

7.16   **The glow discharge.**   The condition in which space charge distorts the field is known as a *glow discharge*. The name comes from the light emitted by the discharge (the light emitted by a Townsend discharge is generally too feeble to be seen) and the region of its origin is shaded on Fig. 7.1. Most of the light is emitted from the region near the anode where there is little field—this is the *positive column*, and is a region of plasma. Near the cathode is the *Crookes dark space*, with the *negative glow* beyond it. The dark space represents the length of electron path before enough energy is accumulated to excite a molecule. If the pressure is reduced, the dark space expands, eventually filling the whole tube.

As the current in a glow discharge increases, the discharge spreads over the surface of the cathode, and the voltage drop across the tube remains unchanged. The current density in the plasma is constant throughout, in accordance with the conditions of stability of the plasma (Section 7.5).

7.17   **Cold cathode tubes.**   The properties of a glow discharge are employed in practice in *cold cathode tubes*. Of these the neon voltage-stabilizer is the most common and it is a direct application of the constant voltage characteristic of the discharge. The cathode is a cylinder with a central anode in the form of a rod. As the current increases the area of the cathode covered by the discharge also increases and the potential drop across the tube remains the same.

In the dekatron counting tube there is a central anode with ten separate cathodes spaced around it. A discharge is initially struck between the first cathode and the anode, and the glow enables its position to be clearly seen. On receipt of a pulse, the discharge can be transferred to the next cathode by way of intermediate electrodes, and so on, so that the total number of pulses may be counted.

In the gas switch a glow discharge between two electrodes is established by the microwave power generated by a transmitted radar pulse, and this effectively short-circuits the receiver while the aerial is transmitting. After the pulse, de-ionization of the gas in the gap is sufficiently rapid for the receiver to be able to accept the reflected signal. In this case the discharge is one of high frequency. Note that a high frequency discharge does not require electrodes in the gas, since the electrons in the gap are impelled on an oscillatory path by the field.

In the d.c. discharge of course the electrodes are vital, since charge is continually being removed, and the cathode itself must be the source of electrons sustaining the plasma. The cathode fall is always determined by the process producing these electrons. There is little voltage drop in the plasma but there will be a small *anode* fall where the electrons finally leave the discharge, and the current in this region is probably space-charge limited.

7.18 **The arc discharge.** If the current in a glow discharge is increased until the whole of the cathode area is covered, the current density in the discharge is finally increased and we are dealing with an *abnormal glow discharge*. At some point in this region, the current through the discharge will suddenly increase, while the voltage drop decreases until the cathode fall is of the order of the ionization potential. According to the definition given in Section 7.7 we are now dealing with an *arc*. The cathode fall clearly determines the energy which an electron must gain in order to maintain the plasma alone—the electrons themselves do not have to be produced by a Townsend process. The electrons in an arc can be produced in different ways, as familiar examples indicate. In the carbon arc the temperature of the cathode spot approaches 4000°C and there is little doubt that the electrons are released by thermionic emission. In the low pressure mercury arc, on the other hand, the cathode spot continually moves over the surface of the liquid mercury, and its temperature does not exceed 200°C, certainly not high enough for thermionic emission. The electrons are thought to be liberated here by field emission. A high field at the cathode is set up, and although classically there is no reason for an electron to leave the potential well which the metal provides, according to quantum mechanics there is a finite probability of an electron penetrating the barrier, and emerging into the vacuum (Section 11.10).

7.19 **Hot cathode arcs.** A thermionic cathode offers an easy solution to the problem of producing electrons in a gas discharge. An example of the hot cathode arc is the thyratron, discussed in Section 7.7. Note that since a glow discharge is governed by the characteristic process of electron emission from the cathode, a hot-cathode glow discharge is a contradiction in terms.

7.20 **The mercury arc rectifier.** The arc, being a high-current, low voltage device, has widespread practical applications in addition to the thyratron. The mercury arc rectifier is widely used as a means of producing a d.c. supply from a.c. mains. Installations of this type may be very large when required for industrial or traction applications. For single units rated above 500 kW, the enclosing vessel is a continuously pumped steel tank, with a mercury pool forming the common cathode for a number of anodes each connected to one phase of a polyphase supply, the arc transferring from one anode to the next. If the current falls below a few amps, the arc is extinguished, and special means for striking it have to be provided. This may be done by an electromechanical device which withdraws an auxiliary anode from the cathode pool to strike the arc, or by the use of separate 'keep alive' anodes supplied with a high d.c. potential.

7.21　The ignitron.　A development of the arc starting problem is the *ignitron*, in which an igniter rod of silicon carbide or boron carbide makes permanent contact with the mercury pool. As mercury does not wet these refractory semiconducting materials, a positive voltage pulse on the igniter rod will intitiate a number of small arcs which are then transferred to the main anode. The cold-cathode arc is controlled by the voltage on the igniter rod in the same way that the thyratron discharge is controlled by the grid potential, and the range of applications of the ignitron is similar.

7.22　Sodium and mercury vapour lamps.　*Hot cathode* arcs are important in lighting. Sodium and mercury vapour streetlamps make use of arcs in the respective vapours, the pressure being maintained by the presence of excess of the element. The pressure will then depend on the operating temperature, and this usually requires that the discharge vessel be insulated thermally by an evacuated outer envelope. The lamps are designed for a.c. operation, and have an oxide thermionic emitter at each electrode, maintained at its operating temperature by the discharge itself. The discharge is started by a high voltage pulse derived by the breaking of an inductive circuit by a thermal switch, the discharge being established in neon gas added to the tube, until the vessel warms up sufficiently to evaporate the mercury or sodium.

Sodium lamps can only be run at low pressure (0·001 mmHg). Most of the radiation emitted is in the visible region, but if the pressure is raised the light is reabsorbed in the vapour surrounding the arc.

Mercury vapour at low pressure emits mostly ultra-violet radiation, but but this can be converted to visible light of chosen colour by the fluorescent material lining the walls of the fluorescent lamp. On the other hand, a mercury arc at high pressure (5 atmospheres and more) is not only a more efficient emitter of radiation, but it produces a high proportion of visible light, whose source is a compact region between the electrodes. The discharge runs at a high temperature and a quartz containing-vessel is required to withstand it.

REFERENCES

PENNING, F. M. *Electrical Discharges in Gases*, Macmillan, London (1957).

PROBLEMS

7.1 An electron of mass m strikes an atom of mass M. What is the maximum energy transfer in an elastic collision?

7.2 A monoenergetic beam of electrons is projected into helium gas at 1 mm pressure, and the electron energy is increased. No energy loss of electrons traversing the gas is recorded until the electron energy is 19·5 V. At this point the electrons lose all their energy but no radiation is emitted. When the electron energy is raised to 20·5 eV, ultraviolet emission at 600 Å is observed. Comment on these results.

7.3 Ultraviolet light of wavelength 500 Å falls on atomic hydrogen. With what velocity will the ejected electron leave? (Ionization potential of H is 13·58 V.)

7.4 Adapt the analysis of Section 3.9 to calculate a value for the mean free path of an *electron* in argon at 1 mm pressure and 300°K (diameter of argon atom: $2·88 \times 10^{-10}$m).

7.5 A planar diode with a photoemissive cathode is to be used as a photocell, and the photocurrent is to be amplified by electron multiplication in a gas. To this end the diode contains gas with a first Townsend coefficient of 150. What electrode spacing will be required to give an amplification of 5?

7.6 The minimum sparking potential of a gas at 0·4 mmHg pressure occurs at an electrode separation of 1 cm, and has the value 300 volts. At a separation of 1 mm, the sparking potential will be 2000 volts for *two* pressures, 1 mm and 150 mm.

  Assuming that the Paschen curve is given approximately by two intersecting straight lines on a log-log plot through the points defined above, at what electrode separation will the sparking potential be a minimum at 0·05 mm pressure, and at what separations will the gas break down at 700 volts and 5 mmHg?

7.7 A gap of 0·5 cm between parallel plane electrodes in a gas is observed to break down at 150 volts applied. The electron multiplication coefficient is 4·6 cm^{-1}. Assuming that the secondary process is electron emission from the cathode, how many secondaries are produced by each positive ion at breakdown?

7.8 An alternating voltage is applied to the anode of a thyratron. If the deionization time of the thyratron is 10^{-3} sec, estimate the maximum frequency this voltage can have for the grid to retain control after every half cycle.

Chapter 8

Gaseous Plasma—Some Applications

8.1 **Scope of the chapter.** A gas in which a significant number of atoms or molecules are ionized, but which is electrically neutral on the macroscopic scale, is known as a *plasma*. The establishment and maintenance of a plasma is important in the conduction of electricity through gases, discussed in Chapter 7, but we will be concerned here with the properties of this condition of matter considered for their own sake.

Gaseous plasma is an unfamiliar state under normal terrestrial conditions, but it is widespread in nature, once one moves away from the earth's surface. In fact it was astrophysical and geophysical phenomena which led first to the considerable study of plasma theory. The scope of this kind of work will be mentioned briefly at the end of this chapter, but for the moment we shall be more concerned with practical developments stemming from the theory.

An apology is called for here. The practical potentialities of those aspects of electron physics considered elsewhere in this book have already been realized in working devices. On the other hand the topics to be discussed in this chapter are far—perhaps very far—from realization. They are worthy of mention not only by virtue of their intrinsic interest, but also because of the world-wide effort on a large scale that is being devoted to their investigation. We find ourselves in one of those sensitive areas where technical achievement is tangled with political issues and with national prestige, and humdrum economic criteria of success diminish in importance.

8.2 **Magnetohydrodynamic power generation—ionization in hot gases.** A large and important part of the energy requirements of mankind are met by the combustion of so-called fossil fuels, coal and oil, and the conversion of the heat so produced into other forms of energy. This process is deplorably inefficient, in large measure as a consequence of the second law of thermodynamics. Ideally we might hope to oxidize our fuel reversibly, as in the *fuel cell*, but even without such a radical improvement there is much that can be done. For instance, one might still feel that the flow of energy in a modern power station, from coal to steam to mechanical linkage with an alternator, could be simplified and improved if fewer stages were involved. One possible method, producing electricity by thermionic means, was mentioned in Section 4.16, and another possibility is to harness thermoelectric effects. We shall discuss here a third method. The fact has long been recognized that flames—and hot gases in general—conduct electricity, and this is recognized as a consequence of the thermal ionization of a small proportion of the atoms present at the temperatures concerned. In other words, we can produce a gaseous plasma non-electrically by going to the upper range of those temperatures attainable by the release of chemical energy. If it is possible to separate the oppositely charged particles in a plasma, a potential difference will be set up, and the work done in the separation can be made available as energy in an external circuit with this e.m.f.

8.3 **The MHD effect and its application.** The separation can be brought about by the *magnetohydrodynamic* effect, which is similar in some respects to the Hall effect familiar in metals and semiconductors (Section 10.8). When a charged particle moves perpendicular to a magnetic field it experiences a force perpendicular to the field and to the direction of motion. In a flowing plasma with electrons and positive ions drifting in the same direction, the forces on electrons and positive ions will be opposed and will cause them to separate to opposite sides of the containing vessel. The charge separation so produced will give rise to electrostatic forces opposing the magnetic deflection, so that an equilibrium is attained with a difference of potential across the vessel. This potential difference is known as the MHD voltage, which can act as the e.m.f. in an external circuit. The power which can be drawn from the external circuit is proportional to

$$\frac{v^2 B^2}{(a+1)\rho},$$

where v is the plasma velocity, B the magnetic flux density, a the ratio of the resistance of the plasma to that of the external circuit, and ρ is the resistivity of the plasma.

For maximum power we need a high magnetic field. Practical considerations set a limit at 1 weber/m². The plasma will consist of hot gases produced by burning a natural fuel in air; by passing the combustion products through a convergent-divergent nozzle, flow velocities approaching the velocity of sound can be attained. The value of ρ depends critically on the resistivity of the plasma. The concentration of ions present will be governed by a Boltzmann distribution (Section 3.11) and will be proportional to $\exp\left(-E_i/kT\right)$ where T is the absolute temperature, and E_i the ionization potential of the gas. The number of ions present gives a resistivity of the plasma that is marginal for our purposes, but if a material with a low ionization potential, such as caesium ($E_i = 3.89$ eV) is compared with 13·62 and 14·54 volts (for atomic oxygen and nitrogen respectively) the position is much improved. For this purpose the combustion gases must be 'seeded' with a caesium compound. Even so, to achieve sufficient ionization temperatures around 2500°K are required, and this is difficult to attain, the more so since passage through the nozzle naturally cools the gas. It should be emphasized that the problem of getting satisfactory power output from an MHD generator is still far from solved. There are formidable practical difficulties, for instance the walls of the gas duct are required to withstand a very high temperature, and the recombination of ions that takes place at them represents a loss of plasma conductivity. Finally, the cost of seeding the very large volumes of gas with caesium becomes high unless steps are taken to recover the caesium from the exhaust gases, which adds an extra degree of complexity. No solution to these difficulties is in sight, but enough has been said to indicate the general direction of the work. For details of developments the reader should consult Reference 2 at the end of the chapter.

8.4 Nuclear fusion—the potentialities of nuclear energy.

In the previous section we considered an unconventional means of producing electrical energy, but the starting point was familiar enough: the release of chemical energy stored in a fossil fuel. This energy is stored as potential energy associated with a given arrangement of atoms, some of which is released in the rearrangement brought about by oxidation. The amount of energy available is 210·8 kcal/mole (~ 20 eV/molecule) for methane. The figure is probably not far from the limit available by the release of chemical energy, though it is of course possible in principle to use this energy in a reversible process, to far better advantage than by combustion.

8.5 The release of energy—general considerations.

How are the atomic rearrangements we have been discussing brought about? They will take place if the temperature is raised sufficiently to permit intermolecular collisions of sufficient violence (Section 3.12). The process of lighting a fire is merely the most familiar example of this, and it is well known that the necessary starting temperature differs from one fuel to another. Since in using chemical change to release energy as heat, we are usually concerned to obtain our energy at the highest possible temperature, this approach is sufficient. It is important to bear in mind that chemical reactions can often be made to 'go' at much lower temperatures in the presence of a suitable *catalyst*, which facilitates the chemical change without being itself directly involved. Thus, a mixture of hydrogen and oxygen will remain unchanged indefinitely at room temperature, but reaction will occur at the surface of finely divided platinum. Catalysis is of the utmost value when we are making use of a chemical reaction for the sake of preparing a new product, and not just for the release of energy.

8.6 **Application to nuclear energy.** The forces which bind neutrons and protons together in a compound nucleus are different in nature from, and $\sim 10^6$ times stronger than, the electrostatic forces between electrons and nuclei which have hitherto been our sole concern. The range of chemical compounds represents the stable atomic configuration permitted by these forces, and in the same way, the stable nuclei represent the possible stable configurations which neutrons and protons can attain under the forces which bind them. If we can bring about nuclear rearrangements in a controlled way, as we can atomic rearrangements, a vast new reservoir of energy becomes available.

8.7 **The nuclear reactor.** The nuclear reactor provides us with a specialized kind of access to this store of energy—by the fission process. This is a nuclear 'reaction', 'catalysed' by neutrons, with the additional feature that the neutrons are themselves a product of the reaction. As the magnitude of the nuclear forces is so large, the amount of energy released in the fission of a U^{235} nucleus (198 MeV) is, by chemical standards, very large. In the reactor, we are making use of catalysis to release this energy at what is in nuclear terms a very low temperature, but one which is high enough to be conveniently harnessed to the steam cycle of conventional power production practice.

8.8 **Nuclear fusion reactions.** Fission is only one of a multitude of possible nuclear rearrangements, one which we happen to be able to control without too much difficulty. This, and others, would be expected to occur spontaneously at sufficiently high temperatures, without catalysis. It has been recognized for some time that nuclear reactions supply the stars with the energy which they are continuously radiating. The processes which are important here are essentially the building up of more complex nuclei from simple ones; they are usually referred to as nuclear *fusion* reactions, as distinct from the splitting, or *fission* of heavy nuclei. A reaction of this type brought about at high temperature is referred to as a thermonuclear reaction.

Two simple examples of possible fusion reactions are:

$$D + D \rightarrow He^3 \ (0\cdot8 \ \text{MeV}) + n \ (2\cdot5 \ \text{MeV})$$
$$D + T \rightarrow He^4 \ (3\cdot5 \ \text{MeV}) + n \ (14\cdot1 \ \text{MeV})$$

where the symbols D and T both represent nuclei of unit charge, and therefore hydrogen nuclei, but which are both heavy isotopes of mass number 2 and 3 respectively, *deuterium* and *tritium* (Section 2.11).

We have indicated in the brackets the amount of energy released in these reactions in the form of kinetic energy of the products, and it is seen to be very large. The uncontrolled release of this energy is readily achieved in the so-called 'hydrogen bomb' where a fission reaction is used to detonate the fusion by providing the necessary high temperature.

8.9 **The need for new power resources.** Why should controlled nuclear fusion be of any practical interest? We can certainly see the end of world resources of conventional fuels, and yet our energy needs are constantly increasing (and will do so more rapidly as standards in the underdeveloped countries are raised). The possibilities of fission power extend our perspectives, but supplies of uranium are not inexhaustible. In addition, there is always in the case of fusion power a marginal element of danger that a rapid (bomb-like) release of energy should accidentally occur. Most seriously, fission is obnoxious in producing among its reaction products a number of unstable (radioactive) nuclei of very long lifetime which represent a costly present problem and a growing and unwelcome legacy to future generations.

The radioactive products of fusion reactions are short-lived, so the process is inherently 'cleaner' than fission. Above all, the abundance of hydrogen on the earth's surface is so great that the problem of exhaustion of fuel supplies becomes trivial.

8.10 **Conditions for the occurrence of fusion.** What conditions must be met for nuclear fusion to take place? Briefly, we require to take a volume of gas containing D (or D and T) nuclei, and raise it to a suitable temperature. In view of the magnitude of nuclear forces, this temperature will be very high, of the order 10^8°K. This is equivalent to 'lighting the fire'. If the ensuing release of energy is to recompense us for the cost in energy of attaining these temperatures, the conditions must be sustained at this temperature for a time of the order minutes. Now, any gas at this temperature will be almost completely ionized, hence the relevance of fusion to this chapter.

Temperatures of one hundred million degrees are so far above anything previously attained that the feasibility of pursuing the proposal further may well be questioned. On the other hand, the kinetic energy of a nucleus at this temperature is only of the order 50 keV, and accelerators producing beams of particles with energies many powers of ten higher than this are a commonplace, which at least indicates that it is easy in principle to supply large quantities of energy to a charged particle. (It should be noted that we cannot bring about a significant number of fusions by the interaction of two colliding beams, since the probability of two nuclei colliding is negligibly small. We definitely require a gas with a *random* velocity corresponding to 50 keV.) Experience with gaseous discharges (Section 7.6) indicates how a plasma can be obtained, in which the ion temperature is high. A suitable starting point for the attainment of very high temperatures is therefore provided by a discharge tube, through which is passed a pulse of very high current; this can be done, for example, by discharging through it a bank of condensers.

The temperature of the plasma will only rise high enough if energy dissipation can be curtailed during the heating. The chief agent of energy loss in a plasma is conduction to the walls of the containing vessel by collision of the ions with the walls. Thus the chief problem to be solved is to find non-material walls—the problem of *containment*.

8.11 **Feasibility of controlled fusion.** The feasibility of this seem-ingly impractical requirement becomes apparent if we consider a charged particle moving in a magnetic field, perpendicular to its direction of motion. The particle will be deflected into a circular orbit (we have seen numerous examples of this already) and so will be 'trapped' in the region of the magnetic field. There is a limitation to this arrangement: if the particle velocity has a component along the magnetic field, this component is un-affected by the field, and the simple magnetic 'container' is merely a cylinder with no ends.

The container can be provided with ends by changing the magnetic field configuration at the ends as shown in Fig. 8.1; an ion approaching the end is reflected back along the axis, and we speak of a magnetic 'mirror'.

Alternatively, the cylinder may be bent round upon itself, so that it

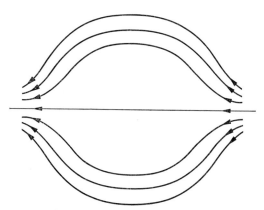

FIG. 8.1 A charged particle moving inside the magnetic field configura-tion represented in cross section above will be deflected so as to prevent its escape. The particle is reflected inwards by this 'magnetic mirror'.

has no ends; in this case, however, the magnetic field in the resulting torus is no longer uniform across the section of the tube, and in consequence ions are deflected to the walls. Some improvement can be effected by twisting the torus into a figure of eight, as in the so-called 'stellerator'; nevertheless there are still residual difficulties which prevent efficient containment, and the realization of the temperatures needed for fusion.

8.12 **The pinch effect.** A different technique of containment depends on the magnetic field of a current flowing in the plasma itself. The magnetic field will exert an inward pressure which will tend to squeeze the current flow away from the walls of the containing vessel, and a very high current gas discharge will leave the walls of the vessel, and be 'pinched' into a narrow channel. This would be very promising if the pinch were stable, but in fact it begins to swell or wobble soon after its formation, until it strikes the walls and is thereby cooled.

8.13 **The present state of fusion research.** Extensive research on each of these projects has already been carried out. No convincing demonstrations of the occurrence of thermonuclear reactions have been given (though there have been 'false alarms') and there are grave difficulties in the way of all methods of magnetic containment which have so far been examined. Much work will have to be done before there is sufficient understanding of plasma physics for further progress. The formidable problem of how to extract the energy produced by thermonuclear reactions has scarcely yet been considered. This and a number of other technical problems concerned with introducing new fuel and removing spent material, show clearly enough to what extent the investigation and exploitation of thermonuclear fusion is a long-term development, of which we are still dealing with the intial stages.

8.14 **Ionic propulsion of rockets.** The success of a rocket motor consists in imparting to a gas stream the maximum possible momentum. The best that can be achieved is that the random motion of the gas should be transformed into an unindirectional stream with the appropriate thermal velocity. In a conventional rocket, this is brought about by the energy released in a high temperature chemical reaction. It is not difficult to accelerate a stream of ions in an electric field, to much higher velocities than can be achieved chemically, so as to obtain in principle a thrust per unit weight of fuel 20 times that attainable conventionally. For instance, a stream of Cs ions could be accelerated in a 'gun' with electrodes at a negative potential with respect to the source. A suitable source would be a structure of porous tungsten impregnated with caesium. The electrical neutrality of the rocket would be maintained by spraying electrons into the ion beam from the rocket nozzle at an appropriate rate. A useful thrust could only be attained at high altitudes where the mean free path of the ions is sufficiently large; even so, for propulsive purposes the thrust needed would require prohibitively large ion currents ($\sim 10^6$ amp). The system has promise as a source of auxiliary thrust, i.e. for the attitude control of space vehicles.

An alternative proposal is concerned with the production of a plasma and its subjection to a rapidly growing magnetic field; it is compressed as it were by a magnetic 'piston,' and may then be directed at high velocity through the nozzle of the rocket.

A considerable amount of preliminary work on these and other projects has been carried out. For details, the reader is referred to the references at the end of the chapter.

8.15   **The geophysical significance of plasmas.**   The introduction of beyond-the-horizon wireless telegraphy by Marconi, besides its obvious practical potentialities, raised important scientific issues, notably the problem that the observed signal strength was greater than could be explained by diffraction of the waves around a spherical earth. Heaviside suggested that there must be a reflecting layer in the atmosphere to return electromagnetic energy to the earth's surface.

The only feasible reflecting layer is a region of ionized gas. The electrons present (say n per unit volume) will execute forced vibrations and so emit secondary waves, with the consequence that the velocity of propagation of the wave is modified. This can be expressed in terms of a refractive index

$$\varepsilon - \frac{ne^2}{m\omega^2\varepsilon_0}$$

For a particular frequency this will be zero; at this frequency and below it electromagnetic energy will be totally reflected. This relationship is the key to a considerable understanding of the properties of the ionized layer, gained by an investigation of the reflection of radio waves (the techniques developed for this purpose were the forerunners of radar).

In this way it was found that there are in fact three ionized layers in the high atmosphere, with successively higher electron densities, from the D layer at 80 km, through the slightly higher E layer, to the F layer at 250–300 km, with a density of 6×10^{11} electrons/m^3.

A characteristic of these layers is their daily fluctuation. The electron density of the D layer is too low to reflect waves of manageable wavelength, but it does attenuate long radio waves quite severely, and long-wave radio communication is more effective at night when the electron density in the layer is a minimum. The F layer shows the most striking diurnal change— during the daytime it splits into two components.

H

The source of the layers is the photoionization of the atmospheric gases by solar radiation. The radiation from the sun extends into the X-ray region at its short wavelength extremity. This radiation cannot be detected at the earth's surface simply because it has been absorbed higher up. The ionized layers—collectively described as the *ionosphere*—are a consequence of this absorption. The dependence on the sun's activity is shown by the ionospheric disturbance accompanying a solar flare, and the dislocation of long range radio communication to which it gives rise.

Although the influence of the ionosphere on radio propagation is the most obvious practical consequence of the ionization, there are other physical effects of interest and importance. The atmosphere is subject to tidal forces due to sun and moon as are the oceans, but for the atmosphere the sun's influence is dominant due to a near-resonance with the natural period of atmospheric oscillation. The movements of the plasma involved in the tidal action produce magnetic effects which are seen as a diurnal variation of the earth's magnetic field. During the night, partial recombination occurs in the plasma, and the emission of radiation which accompanies it can be identified as the *airglow* in the night sky. The more spectacular emissions constituting *aurora polaris* follow excitation caused by streams of charged particles emitted by the sun, which are deflected away from the equator by the earth's magnetic field. On the other hand, surrounding the magnetic equator but at a distance of several earth radii are the recently discovered radiation belts, consisting of charged particles trapped by the earth's magnetic field just as we attempt to contain high temperature plasma for fusion experiments.

In all these aspects, the properties of gaseous plasma are of geophysical importance. Now that rocket and satellite investigations of the high atmosphere are possible, there is an improved chance of seeing all these phenomena as part of a total pattern of changes wrought in the earth's atmosphere by the sun's radiation—with the more familiar meteorological phenomena as an integral part.

In more remote regions, the properties of plasmas in electric and magnetic fields seem likely to give a clue to the nature of sunspots, and also the origin of cosmic radiation. The resurgence of interest in plasmas which we have surveyed in this chapter is certain to further our understanding of these things.

REFERENCES

1. LANGMUIR, D. W. and HERSCHBERGER, W. D. *Foundations of Future Electronics*, McGraw-Hill, New York (1961).

2. McGRATH, I. A., SIDDAL, R. A. and THRING, M. W. (Eds.), *Advances in Magnetohydrodynamics*, Pergamon Press, Oxford (1963).

3. *Proceedings of the Institute of Radio Engineers* **48**, No. 4 (Space Electronics Issue) (1960); **49**, 12 (Plasma Issue) (1961).

Chapter 9

Electronic Conduction in Solids

9.1 The recognition of electronic conduction in solids. The most obvious electrical property of a solid is its electrical conductivity, and it is with this topic that we shall concern ourselves in the next two chapters. An atomic theory of electricity requires that electrical conductivity shall involve the transport of some kind of particles; the first task is to find out which particles are of importance here. A fundamental experiment carried out by Tolman in 1916 provides an answer, by supplying the value of e/m for charge carriers in a crystal. Charge separation was brought about by the rapid rotation of the specimen (a metal), care being taken to exclude effects due to electromagnetic induction. Such separation must therefore be due to the effect of centrifugal force on the charge carriers, this force being balanced by the electrostatic effect of the charge separation. Hence it was possible to calculate e/m for the charge carriers, and the resulting value was in good agreement with that for the electron obtained by Thomson. From this we can conclude that the charge carriers in metals are in fact electrons. In those materials which consist of ions, positive and negative, such as the alkali halides, it is conceivable that electrical conductivity could be due to the migration of ions, and not electrons. Instances of this behaviour do occur, but they are relatively unimportant, since the ions are rarely free enough to move through the crystal lattice at an appreciable rate, except at high temperatures. When ionic conduction does occur, it is easily recognized, since the flow of current is accompanied by the deposition of neutralized ions near the electrodes, in the same way that electrolysis of a solution is accompanied by chemical changes at the electrodes. There is one case of ionic transport in a crystal that is of great practical importance, in an indirect way—the photographic process in silver bromide and iodide is the result of subtle interplay of electron and ion motion in the crystal, both in the production of the latent image, and in its subsequent development. This cannot be discussed here, but an account of the physics of the process is to be found in Reference 2 at the end of the chapter.

9.2 The range of observed conductivities. We can conclude that, in most instances, electrical conductivity of solids is the result of electron motion. The first point to note is the wide range of conductivities found, from $6·7 \times 10^5$ mho m^{-1} for silver at 0°C to 5×10^{-24} mho m^{-1} for rhombic sulphur (conductivity being defined by l/RA, where R is the resistance of a rectangular specimen of length l and area of cross section A). Considering now the energy required to remove an electron from a free atom, this is in the range $3·89$ eV for caesium to $24·5$ eV for helium; it is difficult to see how the very wide range of conductivities actually found could arise directly from these values. Furthermore, the amount of energy required to release an electron from an atom is large, and there is no evidence that conduction electrons require any assistance from the field or in any other way before they are released.

9.3 **The scope of the problem.** In dealing with the conduction of electricity in a gas, we were able to treat the motion of electrons and positive ions as independent except at collisions. In passing from the gaseous to the condensed state (liquid or solid) the mean separation of the atoms decreases from ~ 30 Å in the gas to ~ 3 Å in crystals; at separations so small, it is unrealistic to regard interaction as being confined to collisions. Instead the collective behaviour of all the atoms—indeed strictly of all the nuclei and electrons separately considered—must be investigated. Without simplifying assumptions, the detailed dynamics of an assembly of $\sim 10^{29}$ particles/m^3 is a daunting theoretical problem. The first measure of simplification is provided by the ordered structure characteristic of a crystalline solid. Unless we can presuppose this order, we can make no headway; as witness the present level of our understanding of electrical conduction in liquids and amorphous solids, which lack such long-range regularity.

9.4 **Restriction to crystals.** It is for this reason that our attention must perforce be confined to crystalline solids. This is less restrictive than it seems because all metals, and many insulators, exhibit a well-defined crystal structure. For the present purpose the only aspect of the crystal which is important is the fact that the entire crystal can be built up by the regular superposition of identical units, each containing a small number of atoms, so that these *unit cells* resemble an ordered stack of bricks. In other words, as we imagine ourselves to move through the crystal lattice in any direction, we shall repeatedly find ourselves in surroundings indistinguishable from our starting point, so that the structure exhibits a *spatial periodicity* (Section 3.15).

9.5 **Electronic conduction in terms of chemical bonds.** It is possible to see the regularity so characteristic of the crystal as a consequence of the chemical bonding of different atoms considered in Chapter 3. In ionic crystals the regularity arises from the need for ions of opposite charge, and in general of different sizes, to be ranged as close together as possible (thereby minimizing their electrical potential energy); in covalent crystals, the regularity expresses the directionality of the shared electron bonds. This view has much to commend it, but it has limitations for our present purpose. For one thing, as already mentioned, it gives us little assistance in understanding that most important class of crystals, the metals (Section 3.17). In addition, the models of crystal structure we have just described do not appear to offer any scope for electron motion at all—the electrons are all fixed at specific sites in the crystal. This is not quite so serious as it appears because it is only true of the electronic ground states in the crystal. It is possible to imagine excited states in a crystal such as germanium, in which the excitation is transferred from one atom to another—or, in other words, an electron may be released from an electron-pair bond to wander freely about the crystal. This has similarities to the ionization of a single atom, but there are also differences, for the 'free' electron is still within the crystal, but the real difficulty is that our viewpoint provides no easy way of calculating how much energy will be required to 'free' an electron in this manner.

Clearly the electron, once freed, can participate in the conduction process, and it can be referred to as a charge carrier or, more simply, 'carrier'. This title would be unnecessary were there not other possible carriers, but the release of an electron from a covalent bond provides a further opportunity for charge movement, because an electron from a perfect bond can jump to occupy the vacancy left in the first bond, and so on. This redistribution of electrons over the valence bonds is clearly quite distinct from any movement of the 'free' electrons; in discussing it, for reasons that will be clear later, it is simpler to fix attention on the missing space and discuss the transport in terms of a different carrier, the 'positive hole'. Here once more our theory based on chemical bonding is not helpful, and we can do nothing to calculate the motion of these holes.

We have been talking in terms of the purely covalent bonds in germanium, but what has been said is equally applicable to an ionic crystal. In sodium chloride for instance, we might associate *electronic* conduction with an excited state in which one electron in the crystal is transferred from a chloride ion to a sodium ion. This electron can now jump to any neighbouring sodium ion, and the 'hole' can jump to a neighbouring chloride ion.

9.6 **The need for an alternative approach.** To go beyond this point we shall have to consider an alternative formulation of the problem, better attuned to our needs. If this seems a rather fickle procedure, the reader should remember that most worthwhile physical problems can only be tackled by crudely approximate methods. Now if our technique is good, the answers given to a problem by different approximations should be close to each other and therefore presumably to the 'correct' answer. But if our approximational technique is poor, this convergence will be less apparent, and this, in general, is the situation in which we find ourselves. Our approximations are so crude that it is often not clear that two different formulations refer to the same problem. Thus an approach to crystal structure based on the idea of chemical bonds *should* give us the information we require about electrical conductivity, but does not, because we cannot progress far enough. We shall shortly consider an alternative which will give us important information about conductivity almost at once, but which cannot be seen to provide that theoretical description of the structure of, say, the germanium crystal, that is at once obvious from the chemical bonding theory.

9.7 **A new approach stated.**   To see where we should look for our new approach, and before discarding the chemical bond approach, we had better examine the assumptions on which it is based. In discussing chemical bonds, (Sections 3.6 and 3.7) we look at the energy levels of the electrons in the individual atoms making up our molecule or crystal, and try to decide how these are modified by the presence of other atoms in the vicinity. Now there is an assumption involved here, for there is no *a priori* reason to suppose that we can even identify 'free atom' energy levels when dealing with an aggregate. We make the assumption because we have to start somewhere; as we have already seen a valuable insight into chemical combination is thereby obtained.

It would be equally legitimate to adopt an entirely different starting-point—to look for energy levels for the aggregate as a whole *a priori*, instead of trying to 'patch up' the levels of the free atoms. At first sight, this is heroism pushed to the extremes of folly, for we saw in Section 2.11 that we could not find the energies of several electrons moving in the field of a single nucleus without drastic approximations, and now we are setting up a problem which involves, in addition, several different nuclei (in the case of a crystal, in fact, a very large number). We are helped here by a property of the Schrödinger equation, whereby a linear combination of solutions ψ_n of the equation, $\sum_{n=0}^{p} a_n \psi_n$, where $a_1 \ldots a_p$ are constants, is itself a solution. Since our problem, crudely put, is to guess a solution to the Schrödinger equation, our first guess can be shaped in this way, but we must first decide upon the kind of solutions from which we are to build up our linear combination. We might, for instance, choose the wave functions of the constituent atoms for this purpose, and this approach has proved widely successful. Thus the theoretical chemist calculates molecular energy levels in this way, looking for a linear combination of atomic wave functions which will give the molecular arrangement of the lowest energy. The extension of this method to crystals seems at first sight a hopeless task, because of the enormous number of terms to be handled, but in fact it turns out to be easier than for even quite simple molecules.

9.8   **The Bloch solution of the Schrödinger equation.**   The feature of a crystal which leads to this surprising result is the fundamental one of spatial periodicity. Because the crystal lattice repeats itself, then the potential energy term in the Schrödinger equation

$$\frac{\partial^2 \psi}{\partial x^2} + \frac{\partial^2 \psi}{\partial y^2} + \frac{\partial^2 \psi}{\partial z^2} + \frac{2m}{\hbar^2}\,(E - V)\,\psi = 0$$

is a periodic function. and the equation under these circumstances can be shown—as a piece of pure mathematics, involving no physics at all—to have solutions in the form of plane electron waves, modulated by a function u_k with the periodicity of the crystal lattice thus:

$$\psi\,(xyz) = \exp\,[i\,(k_x x + k_y y + k_z z)]\,u_k\,(xyz),$$

where k_x, k_y, k_z are constants (see Section 9.9). These solutions were first investigated by Bloch. If the periodic function is expanded as a Fourier series, we have the linear combination of individual solutions which started our discussion.

9.9   **The electron in a potential well.**   It would be quite wrong to conclude from what has been said so far, that to solve the Schrödinger equation for a crystal like, say, germanium is easy. In fact it is a problem of the greatest difficulty, even when the best of present-day computers can be used. The significance of our approach is rather this: that quite simple though artificial problems can be solved in terms of it, *and that they are found to have important features in common, which they share with more rigorous solutions of more realistic problems.* These common features will tell us what we want to know, and we must first consider a particularly simple problem, which will set the stage for us. Remembering that an electron requires extra energy to enable it to escape from a crystal (Section 4.3), we can regard a metal simply as a potential well, of depth equal to the work function, within which the electrons are free to move. What are the energies of electrons in this 'free electron' system? To simplify matters further, we will suppose the electron motion confined to one dimension, and for this case

$$\psi = A \exp\,(ikx)$$

will be a solution of the Schrödinger equation, where A and k are constants of integration, to be determined by the boundary conditions. As to these, the best model of a crystal is an infinite periodic structure, so that if we take a length L of our linear crystal, the environment at x will be identical with that at $x + L$, and in general with that at $x + nL$. This gives

$$\psi(x) = \psi(x + nL),$$

and this restricts k to the values

$$k = \left(\frac{2\pi}{L}\right) n$$

when n is an integer. We can now use the fact (Section 2.6) that the product $\psi\psi^*$ defines the probability of finding the particle at that point, and since the electron must be somewhere inside the crystal,

$$\int_V \psi\psi^*\, dx\, dy\, dz = 1,$$

where V is the volume of the crystal. This gives $A = 1/L^{3/2}$, which enables us to express acceptable wave functions in the form

$$\psi = \frac{1}{L^{3/2}} \exp\left(\frac{2\pi n x}{L}\right).$$

This is the equation of a plane wave—an electron wave. We may now substitute in the Schrödinger equation to find the corresponding energy, and this is

$$E = \frac{\hbar^2 k^2}{2m} = \frac{\hbar^2}{2m}\left(\frac{2\pi}{L}\right)^2 n^2.$$

Notice that the energy is defined in terms of a *wave number* k, which in turn is restricted, by the boundary conditions, to integral multiples of $2\pi/L$. Each of these k values 'labels' an energy state, so we can regard k as the quantum number appropriate to this kind of problem. When electron spin is taken into account (as it should be, for the reasons given in Section 2.9), there is also a second quantum number to define the electron state completely. The important thing to note is that energy increases as the *square* of the wave number (Fig. 9.1).

This reasoning is not altered if we consider a more realistic three-dimensional model of the crystal, but another aspect of the wave number is brought out. Electron waves are not specified completely by the numerical value of their wavelengths, since the direction of their propagation must also be known, or, in other words, wavelength and hence its reciprocal are *vector quantities*. When the boundary conditions are applied, it is the three components of k whose values must be integral multiples of $2\pi/L$, so the permitted states may be represented on a diagram whose coordinate axes represent the three components of k, and define a so-called 'k space' (Fig. 9.2).

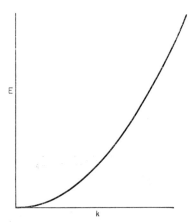

E

k

Fig. 9.1   Graph of electron energy against wave number k for an electron in a one-dimensional potential well.

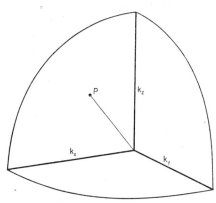

P k_z

k_x k_y

Fig. 9.2   Octant of 'k-space' showing a point P representing the (k_x, k_y, k_z) value of one state. All states on the sphere through P centred on the origin have the same energy $k_x^2 + k_y^2 + k_z^2 = \text{const}$.

The differences between this problem—an electron in a potential box or well—and the problem of the hydrogen atom, are worth noting. In the first place, calculation shows that the energy states are very close together in the box problem ($\sim 10^{-22}$ eV apart) compared with the hydrogen atom

(10·2 eV between the ground state and the first excited state). There is in addition the vector nature of the k quantum numbers, but the significance of this is more clearly seen when we consider the box to be occupied by many electrons.

We can deal with this by a simple extension of our argument, in which we imagine electrons added to the well one by one, the influence of inter-electronic forces being averaged out, and allowed for by slight changes in the depth of the well (which it will be seen does not enter into our answer). The successive electrons are then allocated their states in accordance with the Pauli principle (Section 2.12), which permits two electrons, of opposite spins, to have the same k-value. The states of lower energy will be filled first, i.e. those nearest the origin of Fig. 9.2. When we have added many electrons (and one electron per atom, for a crystal 1 cm cube, would be $\sim 10^{23}$) the occupied states will occupy a spherical volume; the states at the surface are available for further electrons and this leads to the result shown in Fig. 9.3, which represents the increase of the *density of states function*, $N(E)dE$ with k. To represent the number of available states between E and $E + dE$ in this way implies that the available states are *continuous* in the sense of the differential calculus, and not discrete. This will be true to a sufficient approximation, because the states are so close together. In this sense, it is possible to speak of the allowed states as covering a continuous range of energies—as of course do the states of a completely free electron in a vacuum, only here no approximation is involved.

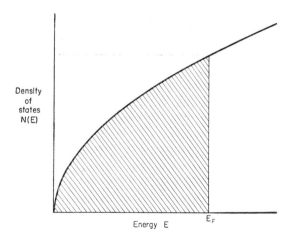

FIG. 9.3   Graph of the density of states function against energy for a crystal. The electrons in the crystal will occupy the states in accordance with the Pauli principle and states up to $E = E_F$ will be occupied.

9.10 **Extension to real crystals—the band theory.** The free electron model is very artificial, and only worthy of the space we have devoted
to it because the same ideas recur in better approximations to a real crystal.
The first stage in the refinement of our argument is to suppose that each
positive ion in the crystal lattice disturbs the potential in the bottom of the
box we have taken to represent the crystal, but that this effect is small, and
only introduces a slight ripple in energy. The effect of this (and we make
use of the Bloch theory discussed in Section 9.8 to calculate it) is striking.
The electron wave number still serves to label the allowed states, but these
no longer form a continuous range over all energies; instead they have finite
gaps at intervals, where there are no permitted states (Fig. 9.4). The density
of states function varies with k in a correspondingly modified way and,
sufficiently close to each gap, it has a parabolic shape, an important fact
we shall return to later. The permitted ranges of energy are referred to as
bands.

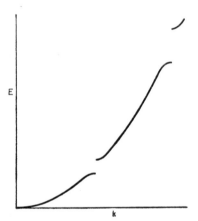

Fig. 9.4 Graph of electron energy against wave number k for an electron
in a one-dimensional periodic potential corresponding to weak binding.
The situation in three dimensions is qualitatively similar. Away from the
gaps, the curve resembles that for 'free' electrons shown in Fig. 9.1.

We can make use of the Bloch theory in another approximation, the
opposite extreme to the one we have just made—that is to assume that the
electrons are tightly bound to their parent atoms, and only slightly disturbed by the presence of neighbouring atoms. Despite the very different
starting point, the results of this calculation are quite similar. The distribution of permitted states for given k are again bands of permitted levels
very close together, separated by gaps free from any allowed levels, the
only difference from Fig. 9.4 being that the gaps are rather wider, and the
bands narrower.

The relationship of these results to each other, to the free electron model, and to the electron bound in an atom, are brought out in Fig. 9.5, which shows a clear progression from the single energy level of the atom, to bands and gaps. The case of the hydrogen molecule (see Section 3.3) is of particular interest; there are two interacting atoms, and resulting from this interaction, two levels arising from a single atomic level. This suggests that in the case of the crystal of N interacting atoms, we should expect to find each band of the crystal to contain N levels. This is indeed the case, even though the reasoning we have followed is too naive (we cannot, in fact, legitimately identify the collection of levels in a crystal energy band with the broadening of any one specific atomic level). This certainly emphasizes how close together the individual levels in a band must be, if N is of the order of 10^{23}, and the total width of the band is of the order of an electron-volt or so.

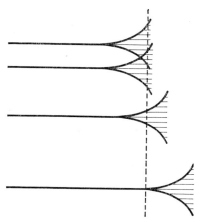

FIG. 9.5 Schematic representation of the effect of interaction on atomic energy levels. The distance between neighbours decreases towards the right of the diagram and causes the levels to split into a group of individual levels close together, whose spread increases as the atoms come closer. Note that for the higher electron states, the spreading begins sooner. The dotted line indicates the equilibrium separation and shows the relation of the 'bands' and 'gaps' to the atomic levels (cf. Fig. 3.1).

9.11 **Experimental confirmation of the theory.** The results of atomic spectroscopy Section 2.10) could be regarded as the most direct experimental confirmation of the theoretical energy level scheme for electrons in an atom, and the levels of electrons in a crystal can be investigated in the same way. We are here chiefly concerned with transitions of electrons from the outer occupied levels of atoms in a crystal (which will be those most influenced by the crystal environment, and those for which the bands are widest) to levels lying close to the nuclei of the atoms in the crystal. Such levels will be screened from outside influences by all the other electrons; hence their energy levels will be very little affected whether the atom is in a crystal or whether it is not, i.e. these levels will hardly be broadened at all. To observe this, electrons must first be ejected from one of the inner levels; the resulting transitions correspond to quanta in the 'soft' (long wavelength) X-ray region of the electromagnetic spectrum. These spectral 'lines' are found to be broadened into bands, as we should expect if our theoretical reasoning was sound.

This experimental evidence, qualitative though it is, gives us confidence to assert that the grouping of energy levels into bands is a perfectly general property of electron energy levels in crystals. This is reasonable on theoretical grounds, for we find the same pattern for the opposite extremes of almost negligible binding of the electrons to their parent atoms, and very tight binding, as we have discussed. Any real crystal will lie within these limits, and may be expected to show the same *qualitative* features. The relatively small number of calculations of the energy levels of real crystals that have been carried out in recent years provide a most satisfactory confirmation of this assertion.

9.12 **Distribution of the electrons over the allowed states.** The simple notion that the energy levels of electrons in crystals are grouped in bands, with finite gaps between, but within a band are very close together, alone provides us with the information we need to deal with the whole question of the electrical conductivity of crystals, and we must now examine the way in which it does so.

To start, we must consider how the electrons are distributed over the available levels. Imagine the electrons added, one at a time, to a crystal 'core' made from the stripped nuclei of the constituent atoms (cf. Section 2.12). Again we can take account of the interaction of one electron on another by allowing each electron to modify slightly the periodic potential field that each electron experiences. This will no doubt affect slightly the numerical factors in the expression for the energy of a given state, but we shall assume as before that the quantum numbers labelling that state will be unchanged. Successive levels will then be filled, in accordance with the Pauli principle (i.e. two electrons of different spin for each level) until all the electrons have been allocated a state. We must then, in logic, have one of the following situations:

(i) The energy levels are filled up to some point partway through one of the bands, with the upper states in the band empty.

(ii) The states are occupied up to the very top of one of the bands, so that a gap without allowed states separates the occupied from the upper, empty levels.

This difference divides crystals into two quite different groups. Group (i) we can identify with the metals, and group (ii) with the insulators. We must now consider how this striking and sweeping distinction comes about.

9.13   Effect of an electric field on electrons in a crystal.

An electric field, acting on an electron in a vacuum, causes it to be accelerated, or, in other words, increases its kinetic energy. Now the electron in a box envisaged in Section 9.9 (in the free electron model) is not in a state differing physically from this, and it too will be accelerated, which here means that it will ascend the 'ladder' of available energy levels. In the case of a crystal the same may be true, but the presence of gaps in the 'ladder' means that an electron must acquire a very large amount of energy to carry it past these obstacles—larger, in fact, than the electron could gain in this way unless very high fields were employed.

In case (i) this will not prevent electrons from gaining energy from the field, from moving and from carrying a current. In case (ii) however, all the permitted states below a gap are already occupied; the exclusion principle allows no scope for any electron to gain energy from the field, since the states to which an electron might jump are occupied. Hence the electrons can make no response to the field, so that class (ii) crystals are insulators; on the other hand those of class (i) are metals. Class (ii) crystals however, may be expected to conduct electricity at very high applied fields, when transitions are possible to the next band; in fact, the phenomenon we meet with here is dielectric breakdown, which limits the performance of any insulator at extreme conditions.

Thus, what we may now describe as the 'band theory' or Bloch approach to crystals leads at once to a natural treatment of electronic conductivity, by explaining the difference between insulators and metals; as implied in Section 9.6 however, we are told nothing we did not already know about the spatial relations of the atoms in the crystal. For this we still need an interpretation based on chemical bonding.

9.14   The electron as a wave packet.

The insight we have gained into conductivity has been gained at a price which we must now examine. In solving the Schrödinger equation for the electron, our solution has the form of a plane wave—modulated, according to Bloch, with the periodicity of the crystal lattice, but a plane wave none the less. We cannot say where the electron is, except that it is somewhere inside the crystal, and since our object is to discuss current flow as the transport of electrons from place to place, this information is quite inadequate. Our probability distribution is quite uniform within the crystal, and to make a comparison with electromagnetic radiation, it resembles a completely monochromatic radiation field. Neighbouring energy states are like similar fields of slightly different wavelength. Now, if we take a number of wave fields of wavelengths within a certain range, the wave motions will superpose; the result will be a cancellation by mutual interference over most of space, with finite resultant amplitude over only a narrow region, a so-called *wave packet*. A commonplace example in the field of electromagnetic radiation is a radar pulse, Fourier analysis of which will reveal not only the carrier frequency but a rich harmonic content, which alone can produce localization of the amplitude in a given region. The profile of the wave packet does not, of course, remain stationary, but is itself propagated through space, in general not with the phase velocity of the constituent waves but with a *group velocity* defined by

$$v_g = 2\pi \frac{dv}{dk},$$

where v is the frequency of the waves (here we are concerned with de Broglie waves) and k is the wave number (Section 9.9).

Now, instead of dealing, as hitherto, with *single* solutions of the Schrödinger equation for a crystal, each characterized by a single k-value, we are equally entitled to consider together a *group* of solutions, with k values over a narrow range. These will constitute a wave packet, and will give a finite amplitude for the wave function only in a limited region of space. Since $\psi\psi^*\ d\tau$ gives the probability of finding an electron in the volume element $d\tau$, we have gone some way to recovering the agreeably concrete idea of a localized electron, and we can achieve this localization to a differing degree, by varying the range dk over which we synthesize the wave packet. All this is far short of the pinpoint localization presupposed by classical electron theory, but the uncertainty principle rules out any possibility of this (Section 2.3). The apparent arbitrariness of the wave packet concept is also clarified by the principle. Thus, with a single energy level, we are considering a definite k value, and hence (through the de Broglie relation) a definite electron momentum, and in consequence we forfeit all knowledge of the whereabouts of the electron within the crystals. If, by considering a wave packet, we are prepared to be indefinite about k to an extent dk, we can achieve a corresponding gain in precision in the localization of our electron.

9.15 The effective mass.

Taking this wave packet as a substitute for the classically precise notion of an electron, what is the action of an electric field F upon it? The group velocity of the packet is changed by the field, and when this is mathematically expressed we have:

$$\frac{dv_g}{dt} = \left(\frac{eF}{\hbar^2}\right) \frac{d^2E}{dk^2}.$$

This relation is important because it is formally so similar to Newton's second law of motion:

$$\frac{dv}{dt} = \frac{eF}{m}.$$

If we write $\hbar^2 \left/ \dfrac{d^2E}{dk^2} \right.$ in the first equation as an *'effective mass'* m^*, the two become identical in form. The significance of this result can hardly be over-emphasized. We have found a method of describing crystals in terms of fundamental theory which gives a clear and immediate distinction between metals and insulators; the drawback is that the theory is formulated in terms of waves, and the intuitive notion of the electron as a perfectly conventional charged particle, which serves us so well in the field of vacuum electronics, has been replaced by concepts that are far less congenial. Yet through the idea of the wave packet it is possible to return to the simplicity of the particle treatment, and—the crucial step forward—we are at once equipped with a prescription for calculating an effective mass of the electrons *so that this quantity alone represents the effect of the perfect crystal lattice on the electron. Once the free electron mass has been replaced by the effective mass, we can treat the electron in the lattice as if it were free, and forget about the lattice altogether.* When the argument is presented in these terms, it is clear that it is no more difficult to think about electron motion in a crystal than it is to think about it in a vacuum.

9.16 **The importance of Ohm's law.** The point of view summarized in the last section represents a valuable simplification. On closer examination, however, it appears slightly suspect, for this reason. It purports to set up an analogy between electron motion in a vacuum, and in a crystal. But electron motion in a vaccuum takes place without any energy loss by the electron, whereas in conduction in a crystal, there is the familiar and inescapable phenomenon of Joule heating, which represents a continual dissipation of energy by the electrons in the crystal, and the direct comparison begins to seem artificial. The Joule energy loss can be referred directly to the idea of an electric current as a stream of particles in the following way. In itself, it is a consequence of Ohm's law, and Ohm's law can arise in an electric current due to a stream of particles if, and only if, the particles move in the field direction with a velocity which is constant, and directly proportional to the field. The constant of proportionality here, $v = \mu F$, is referred to as the *mobility* of the charge carriers. Contrast with this the vacuum situation, where the electrons are accelerated.

A parallel may be drawn here with the acceleration of a free falling body

I

in a gravitational field *in vacuo*. If the vacuum is replaced by a resistive medium, the body will soon attain a fixed terminal velocity. It is the latter case which is comparable to conduction in a crystal.

The idea of mobility can be generally interpreted in terms of collisions which the carrier makes, in the course of which it continually loses the energy gained from the electric field. In the case of a crystal, with what is the electron colliding?

9.17 The behaviour of real crystals—scattering processes. It seems obvious at first sight that the electron will be colliding with the atoms of the perfect lattice, but this cannot be correct. We have taken these into account in assigning a value of effective mass to the electron, where they will determine the value of m^* through the term d^2E/dk^2. There is no place where they could enter the discussion further. We are faced in fact with the embarrassment of a theory which predicts zero resistance for all crystals. Or, strictly, for all 'perfect' crystals, for the distinction is an important one. A real crystal differs from the regular periodic array which we have considered in two ways.

In the first place, no real crystal will ever be perfectly pure, and in the crystal lattice there will be recurrent—but random—sites at which an alien species is situated, having a different potential field from the host atom. It is immaterial whether the sites of the impurities are regular lattice sites or not, and for that matter, an atom missing from the host lattice is equally effective. Any deviations of the potential field from the periodic potential of the perfect crystal will scatter the electron, just as a free electron may be scattered by residual gas atoms in a 'soft' valve.

In the second place, the atoms of a crystal lattice do not remain perfectly still at fixed geometrical points. At a finite temperature, the crystal possesses a certain amount of thermal energy, taking the form of collective vibrations of the constituent atoms. There are a great number of possible modes of vibration of a system built up of so many units as a typical crystal, and a superposition of these is necessary to account for the real motion of the atoms in time. This will give at any instant a picture of the atoms displaced from their average positions according to a calculable pattern. This again can be represented as divergencies from the periodic potential of the perfect lattice, and again will lead to the scattering of a free electron.

It is by virtue of these two scattering mechanisms that a conduction electron in a crystal will only be accelerated by an applied electric field for a certain interval of time, a statistically fluctuating interval whose mean value we will call the *relaxation time* (τ), and will then be scattered by an irregularity of the crystal potential (or will undergo a collision, in other words), so that some of its energy is lost, and the acceleration will start over again. The consequence of this is a constant drift velocity, proportional to the field. This picture of the path of an electron in a field leads at once to the expression

$$\mu = e\tau/m^*$$

linking mobility and relaxation time.

The operation of these scattering processes will be much impeded for very pure crystals at very low temperatures and indeed it is found that the resistance of pure metal single crystals tends to zero as the absolute zero of temperature is approached. (This is altogether distinct from superconductivity, the remarkable property of some metals, of having zero resistivity at a *finite* temperature. This phenomenon can only be explained by interaction of the electrons and the lattice collectively. It is undreamt of in our philosophy).

9.18   The difficulty of a quantitative approach in the case of metals.   If the band theory of crystals is to justify itself, it is hardly sufficient that it should make the kind of qualitative pronouncements with which we have so far been content. It is not enough to say why metals are metals, unless we can also predict, say, the resistivity of a single crystal of copper. In calculations of this sort with metals progress has been disappointing, and the reasons are clear enough. Copper, for instance, has one outer shell or valence electron in each atom. In a crystal, these electrons from each atom constitute a band, which is, with one electron per atom, half full (see Section 9.12). The theory treats each of these electrons as an isolated individual, almost as if the others were not there. It is unlikely that the effects of one electron on another can be dismissed by such crude procedures as averaging over the whole periodic potential. A fair test for the band theory would require a crystal with the conduction electrons much less crowded.

9.19   The difficulty of a quantitative approach in the case of insulators.   The second category, that of insulators, does not appear very promising—the idea of a crystal that *does not* conduct electricity is too negative to be very helpful. However, the band theory picture of an insulator suggests ways in which conductivity could be conferred on these materials.

Consider first the absorption of radiation by a crystal. The absorption will involve the transfer to the crystal of one quantum $h\nu$ of energy at a time, and this energy will be taken up by an electron, which will then be raised to an excited state. In a metal, transitions are possible over a wide range of energies, and all metals do strongly absorb radiation in the visible and infra-red regions of the spectrum, as well as longer (radio) wavelengths. The case of an insulator is more interesting. All transitions are forbidden to electrons by the Pauli principle, except those from a full to an empty band. Thus, for quantum energies that do not encompass the gap above the outermost filled band, no absorption is possible, and the crystal should be transparent. It is found that all non-metals exhibit this region of transparency, which may extend far into the ultra-violet, as in the case of diamond, or only reach the infra-red, as in germanium.

For the more energetic photon which is absorbed, an electron will be raised to a previously empty band, so that this, as well as the no longer filled band from which it came, will be able to contribute to conductivity. Thus an insulator can conduct if it is irradiated with radiation of suitable wavelength. This property, *photoconductivity*, has been recognized experimentally for a long time. It forms the basis of many important radiation detectors. The phenomenon of photoconductivity is interesting and useful, but its details are complicated, and its study does not provide the breakthrough that we require in the study of conductivity.

9.20 **The effect of thermal energy on electron states.** We have previously considered thermal energy only in so far as it affects the instantaneous positions of the ions in a crystal (Section 9.17). For all the attention we gave it, there might as well be no coupling at all between the electrons and the lattice of positive ions. This is of course, not true; the electrons and the positive ions are in thermal equilibrium, with all that it implies. So far as we are concerned, it implies that temperature has an effect on the occupancy of the electron levels. This is something we have ignored, and the arguments we have advanced on this subject properly apply only at $0°K$.

The electrons thus have a part share in the thermal energy of the crystal lattice, which means that at a finite temperature the electrons will no longer occupy the lowest possible energy levels. We can no longer say that, for a given distribution of possible states, those up to a given energy will be filled, and the rest empty, and instead there will be a probability $f(E)$ that a given state is occupied, which can have intermediate values between 0 and 1. The value of $f(E)$ can be calculated in a general way from thermodynamic arguments subject to any restrictive condition apposite to the particular problem under consideration. In the case of electrons in a crystal, the restriction is the Pauli exclusion principle, which prevents the electrons from crowding up beyond the statutory 2 (of opposed spin) per k value. For these circumstances the value of $f(E)$ is

$$f(E) = \left[\exp\left(\frac{E - E_F}{kT}\right) + 1 \right]^{-1},$$

where E_F is a constant; $f(E)$ is known as the *Fermi-Dirac distribution function.* Figure 9.6 shows a plot of $f(E)$ as a function of energy for 0°K, and for two higher temperatures which in fact would be above the melting point of any real crystal. It is seen that the 'blurring' of the occupancy is restricted even at very high temperatures; this is a direct consequence of the Pauli principle. It is for this reason that the contribution of the electrons to the thermal energy makes only an insignificant contribution to the specific heat of a metal (this was a serious stumbling block in the study of electrons in crystals before quantum theory was understood). It means that in metals, the state at 0°K is by no means a bad approximation to the state at room temperature. With certain insulators, this is not true, and it is crystals of this kind that we must now consider.

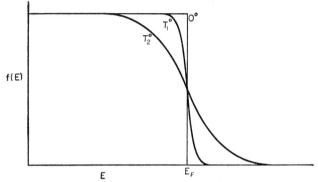

FIG. 9.6 Graph of the Fermi distribution function $f(E)$ against energy for 0°K, T_1°K, and T_2°K where $T_1 < T_2$. To take the example of copper T_1 would be 8400°K and T_2 over 40,000°K which shows that the curve for 0°K is a good approximation to the behaviour of the metal at ordinary temperatures.

9.21 **Semiconductors.** For a metal at 0°K the levels will be filled up to a certain E_F—the *Fermi energy*, and at a finite temperature only states within a narrow region—a few kT—of this will be affected by thermal energy. If we now consider a region of the permitted energy levels above and below the Fermi energy to be annihilated, we have created an energy gap, and transformed our crystal into an insulator. If this gap is not too wide, the 'wings' of the Fermi-Dirac distribution will span it, so that there is a finite probability that states at the bottom of the band that is empty at 0°K will be occupied, and that corresponding states at the top of the ideally filled band will be empty. The number of states involved will be exceedingly small, unless the gap is only a few times kT wide—but since the disturbances we have mentioned confer a conductivity on the crystal where in their absence there is none, we have a simple and very sensitive test for their presence, and a very small number of electrons can make a lot of difference. This is the situation in a number of crystals. Thus in pure germanium, the constant E_F in the distribution function is 0.35 eV†, and about 10^{19} electrons/m³ will be raised to the upper band, only one electron per thousand million atoms in the lattice. Since their mobility is 0.39 m²/volt sec at 300°K this small proportion is sufficient to confer on the crystal a substantial conductivity.

For instance, an electric field of 1 volt/m will cause the electrons to drift in the field direction with an average velocity numerically equal to the mobility. Hence, the amount of charge crossing unit area in the crystal will be equal to that carried by the number of electrons in a prism of unit cross section and height μ, that is

$$i = ne\mu,$$

and, by definition, this will be equal to the conductivity. Now mobility is a quantity that can be determined experimentally (Section 10.8), and as we have seen for electrons in germanium its value is 0.39 m²/volt sec, so this gives, for the conductivity, 0.64 mho m⁻¹. This value, although lower than the value of 6×10^5 for copper, which is typical of the conductivities of metals, is certainly much higher than would justify the description 'insulator'.

The expression above for the conductivity of the crystal shows that the quantity is directly proportional to the number of electrons which are free to carry current, and the exponential form of the Fermi-Dirac distribution function shows that the number of carriers thermally freed will increase rapidly with temperature. This behaviour is quite different from the situation in a metal, where the number of electrons in the unfilled band is not changed by a change in temperature, but where the scattering by thermal vibrations becomes more effective at high temperature, so that the electron mobility and hence the conductivity is reduced.

The distinction between metals and insulators is only clear cut, then, at 0°K. At any higher temperature an insulator is liable to display a finite conductivity, increasing with temperature, the amount of which will be determined by the size of the band gap. Materials behaving in this way have been known for many years, and referred to as *semiconductors*.

The key to the importance of semiconductors is emphasized by the course of the discussion which has led us to consider them. We have evolved a way of handling electrical conduction in crystals in terms of a particle, like an 'ordinary' electron but with mass m^*, the effective mass. In the case of metals, this picture does not help us in more than a very superficial way; it is like trying to understand the conduction of electricity in a gas at high pressure. What is needed is a type of crystal which possesses the simplicity we are forced to assume in the theory. Above all, since the

---

† Energy is measured here from the bottom of the conduction band.

theory is conceived in terms of single, independent electrons, we need a material with a carrier density small enough to approximate to this condition. It is for this reason that semiconductor physics is important. This is not to say that semiconductor *devices* are not important, but to insist that, without a clear and simple picture of conduction such as the band theory provides, most semiconductor applications would have remained undiscovered. In the next chapters the important characteristics of semiconductors and their applications will be developed further.

REFERENCES

1. HUME-ROTHERY, W. *Atomic Theory for Students of Metallurgy*, Institute of Metals, London (1952).

2. MEES, C. E. K. *Theory of the Photographic Process*, 2nd edn., Macmillan, New York, (1954).

PROBLEMS

9.1 A crystal has dimensions a, b, c, parallel to x, y, z co-ordinate axes respectively. Use the Uncertainty Principle to find the limits within which we can establish the momentum of the electrons. If the x, y and z components of the momentum are now represented on a diagram, the state of the crystal is represented by a small cubic cell on the diagram, and this is true of every defined electron state. According to the Exclusion Principle each cell can accommodate two electron states.

By considering the aggregation of the filled cells as electrons are added to the crystal, find

   (i) The Fermi energy for N electrons

   (ii) The density of electron states

   (iii) The average kinetic energy of the electrons

9.2 With reference to the previous question, calculate the Fermi energy for copper (density $8.89 \times 10^3 \text{kg/m}^3$; atomic weight 63.57) gold (1.933×10^4; 197.2) and aluminium (2.699×10^3; 26.97). Find in addition the electron velocity at the Fermi surface in each case.

9.3 How many electrons per m^3 are there in metallic copper, having energies between 7.0 and 7.1 eV, at $0°\text{K}$ and $2500°\text{K}$?

9.4 Find the temperature at which there is a 1% probability of finding an electron 0.3 V above the Fermi energy.

9.5 Calculate the electric current due to the motion of charge carriers of charge $-e$, at a concentration of n/m^3 with a constant velocity v along the field direction. Show that the current satisfies Ohm's law if v is proportional to the field strength. Write down an expression for the conductivity in this case, in terms of the mobility μ. Repeat the calculation for carriers of charge e, density p/m^3 and a different mobility. Finally, consider the case where both species of carrier are present.

9.6 If one electron per atom of copper contributes to the electrical conductivity, which is $5\cdot92 \times 10^7$ mho/m, what is the drift velocity under a field of 1 volt/m?

Chapter 10

Semiconductors

10.1 A simplified energy scheme for semiconductors. A few
of the chemical elements, and a great number of compounds, are found
to exhibit semiconducting properties in the sense discussed at the end
of the last chapter. Of the elements, silicon and germanium from Group
IV of the periodic table are of pre-eminent importance; simple binary
compounds between elements of Group III and those of Group V have a
similar crystal structure, so it is not surprising to find that these also are
semiconductors. Of these compounds, indium antimonide and gallium
arsenide have been extensively investigated and are used in specialized
applications, which will not concern us here; this chapter and the next
refer almost entirely to silicon and germanium.

Since our thinking about conduction in crystals has been determined by
the band theory, it is natural that, in discussing semiconductors, we shall

FIG. 10.1 Representation of electron energy states in a crystal, showing
bands and gaps. The number of levels shown in a band is purely diagrammatic. Note how the lower-lying electron levels are less broadened by
crystal interaction.

wish to refer frequently to a diagrammatic representation of the energy levels. Figure 10.1 would serve for this purpose, but in fact something simpler is sufficient for all situations with which we shall be concerned, and is to be preferred; its use follows a well-established convention in semiconductor work.

There are only two of the energy bands which are of interest—the highest normally occupied band, known as the *valence band* (because it accommodates the outer electrons from each atom in the crystal, the electrons associated with chemical combination or valence), and the lowest normally empty band, called the *conduction band* (for reasons which we hope are obvious). There is no need to indicate any other bands on the diagram. Since we are rarely concerned with states more than a few times **k**T from the inner edges of the two bands, we can simplify further by leaving out the top of the conduction band and the bottom of the valence band; we are then left with Fig. 10.2. In this diagram, the vertical direction is one of increasing electron energy as we go upwards. The horizontal scale has no quantitative significance, but the band edges are drawn as long lines symbolically, to remind us that the levels are the property of the whole crystal. When we have to consider energy levels which pertain to some restricted region of space (localized levels), for instance levels associated with a single atom of an impurity in the crystal (Section 10.4), we can draw the contrast by marking them with short lines. Examples of these localized levels are shown in the diagram.

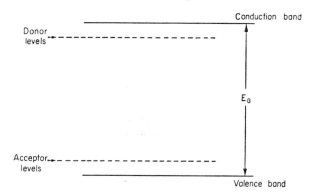

FIG. 10.2 Simplified energy band diagram suitable for the discussion of semiconductors. Both donor and acceptor levels are indicated for convenience; it will be realized that usually one or the other type of impurity will be preponderant.

10.2 **The positive hole.** In the earlier discussion of semiconductors (Section 9.5), as well as in connection with photoconductivity, it was implied that not only would an electron raised to the conduction band conduct electricity, but that the valence band, now no longer filled, would also have a contribution to make. It is one thing to sum the effects of a few electrons in the practically empty conduction band, by identifying wave packets with particles, but to do the same with the valence band, occupied as it is by only a few electrons short of its full complement (of the order of 10^{23}) is another matter.

It can be simplified by a subterfuge. Consider a particularly simple case, a valence band which has lost only one electron. Let us commence with the band completely filled. We know that it cannot make any contribution to the conductivity (Section 9.13). We can transform this into the case which concerns us by adding a purely hypothetical 'anti-particle' which will annihilate one of the electrons in the filled band. The contribution of the unfilled band to the conductivity is the sum of the contribution of the filled band (zero) and that of the anti-particle. The anti-particle must have charge of opposite sign to that of the electron (hence positive), and negative mass (*effective* mass, of course). The behaviour of the almost filled band can be described in terms of the anti-particles alone, which are called *positive holes*. At first sight we are now confronted with the awkward concept of a negative mass, but closer inspection shows that in fact we avoid

that very difficulty. Remembering the effective mass formula $m^* = \hbar^2 \left/ \dfrac{d^2E}{dk^2} \right.$,

and the form of the $E(k)$ curves where electrons in the valence band are free to move, i.e. at the top, we see that there the second derivative is negative (Fig. 9.4); so also, therefore, is the *electron* effective mass, hence the effective mass of the positive hole is positive. Notice that the hole effective mass and the electron effective mass are in general different in

magnitude, since the values of $\dfrac{d^2E}{dk^2}$ for the two bands are not the same. We

can think of the positive hole as a particle able to collide with lattice irregularities in just the same way as an electron, and therefore as having a mobility of its own.

10.3 **Semiconductors—basic principles.** To summarize these fundamentals, we can consider the electrical conductivity of a semiconductor as being due to the motion of two species of carriers: electrons and positive holes. The population of each carrier is fixed by the physical conditions: the nature of the crystal, the temperature, the presence of radiation for instance. In an electric field each kind of particle will drift in the field direction with a velocity (positive or negative) proportional to the field, the constant of proportionality being the mobility. The mobilities of the particles are determined by their collisions, not with ions of the perfect lattice, but with disturbances of this regular periodicity, impurities or thermal lattice vibrations. Apart from these, the particle motion is unaffected by the crystal lattice, provided the correct values of effective mass are used.

In principle, the concentration of each carrier can be calculated from theory, as also its effective mass and mobility; in practice however this is far too difficult, and these quantities are usually regarded as parameters to be determined experimentally, by methods to be discussed in Section 10.8.

10.4 **Intrinsic and extrinsic conductivity.** We have already seen that the concentration of holes and electrons in a semiconductor can be controlled through the temperature (Section 9.21). This is the case of the pure or *intrinsic* semiconductor. The concentrations can also be controlled in a more important way, by making use of the behaviour of impurities in the crystal lattice. In discussing this, germanium will be taken as an example.

An impurity can enter a crystal lattice in two ways.

(i) Provided the impurity atom is small enough, it can fit into the spaces (interstices) between the atoms of the normal crystal lattice. This would be an *interstitial* impurity. These impurities are not of great importance in semiconductors and we shall not discuss them further.

(ii) An impurity atom can also enter the crystal lattice at a regular site, replacing a germanium atom in the pure lattice. This *substitutional* siting is only possible if the impurity atom can form bonds with its nearest neighbours in the same manner as the germanium atom it replaces. Silicon can readily substitute for germanium in this way, but the case of an impurity from Groups III or V of the periodic table it of greater interest by virtue of its far-reaching effect on the electrical properties of the crystal. (It can be shown, by measuring by an X-ray method the distortion of the crystal lattice which the impurities produce, that elements in these groups do enter the germanium lattice substitutionally). We shall consider specific examples.

Group V—arsenic in germanium. The arsenic atom has one electron more than the germanium atom, and the nuclear charge is of course one unit larger. Four of the electrons in the outer shell are required to form electron-pair bonds to the four nearest neighbour germanium atoms. The additional electron merely preserves the electrical neutrality of the arsenic—in other words it is retained by Coulomb attraction—and in a sense resembles the single electron in the hydrogen atom. The situation is very different from that in the hydrogen atom because the impurity here is immersed in a germanium crystal, whose effect we can approximate by regarding it as a continuous medium of dielectric constant $\epsilon \sim 10$.

This reduces the binding energy by $\dfrac{m^*}{m\varepsilon^2}$ so that the binding energy is not the 13·6 eV of the hydrogen atom but 0·01 eV. This energy is so low that at temperatures above about 20°K almost all the arsenic atoms will be ionized, and their electrons released into the conduction band. Hence we can represent the bound state levels of the arsenic atom on the band diagram by short lines below the conduction band (Fig. 10.2). The effect of other impurities from Group V of the periodic table will be similar (for instance, phosphorus or antimony). This type of impurity is a *donor*. Each donor atom incorporated can furnish one electron to the conduction band, so that specimens of germanium can be produced with a controlled population of conduction electrons; these are known as n-type germanium.

Group III—gallium in germanium. A gallium atom entering the germanium lattice substitutionally is one electron short of the number required to form four pair bonds, and there will be a tendency for the atom to make good this deficiency at the expense of the parent crystal, that is to say from the valence band, leaving a positive hole. This hole will only be free to move about the crystal if it can be ionized thermally—this will occur at normal temperatures since the ionization energy is small, as it was for the electron in (i) above. An impurity of this kind is an *acceptor*, and its energy levels can be represented by short lines above the valence band (Fig. 10.2). Other examples of acceptor impurities are boron, aluminium, and indium. A semiconductor with a controlled density of holes furnished by added acceptors is said to be p-type.

Collectively, semiconductor crystals in which the carrier concentration is controlled by added impurities are referred to as *extrinsic semiconductors*.

Substitutional impurities which are not from Groups V or III of the periodic table will also produce localized levels. These will lie deeper than the simple donor and acceptor levels, and there will also be more than one level per added atom, because of the possibility of multiple ionization. These impurities have not yet proved of great technical importance.

If a semiconductor crystal contains a volume density of donors N_D, and a density of acceptors N_A, then it will be n-type if $N_D > N_A$, with a density of donor sites $N_D - N_A$. Electrons from the other N_A donors occupy the acceptor levels, which are said to be *compensated*. It is possible to have a compensated p-type material if $N_A > N_D$ and also possible (at least in principle) for compensation to be exact ($N_A = N_D$).

10.5 The variation of carrier concentration with temperature.

We must now consider in more detail, and including the extrinsic case, the effect of temperature on the carrier concentration in a semiconductor. This is a matter requiring the application of the Fermi-Dirac distribution law (Section 9.20) to the appropriate energy level scheme.

The Fermi-Dirac function is

$$f(E) = \left[\exp\left(\frac{E - E_F}{kT}\right) + 1\right]^{-1}$$

and to use it to calculate the density of electrons in the conduction band we must sum this over all the states. Since the states are close enough to be regarded as a continuum, we can reduce this summation to an integration over the known density of states. This can be done because only states at the very bottom of the band are occupied in a semiconductor (Section 9.21), and over this region the parabolic form of the density of states for the free electron model (Section 9.9) is an acceptable approximation, provided that the free electron mass is replaced by the effective mass. Furthermore, for the conduction band of a semiconductor, the exponential term in the Fermi-Dirac distribution function is usually (see the last paragraph of this section) $\gg 1$. Under these circumstances, the distribution approximates to the classical Boltzmann type (Section 3.11) and simplifies the mathematics considerably. Weighting the density of states with the probability function, and carrying out the integration, the result is found to be

$$n = 2\left(\frac{2\pi m_e^* kT}{h^2}\right)^{3/2} \exp\left(-\frac{E_F}{kT}\right).$$

The terms outside the exponential are frequently written for brevity as N_c, described as the effective density of states in the conduction band.

Now, since a hole is an energy level *not* occupied by an electron, we can adopt an exactly similar procedure to write down the number of holes in the valence band. This is

$$p = 2\left(\frac{2\pi m_h^* kT}{h^2}\right)^{3/2} \exp\left(-\frac{(E_G - E_F)}{kT}\right),$$

or

$$p = N_v \exp\left(-\frac{(E_G - E_F)}{kT}\right),$$

where N_v is the effective density of states in the valence band. Both these expressions contain the constant E_F whose value we do not know. To proceed further we must be more specific. For this purpose consider first the case of an intrinsic semiconductor. In this case each electron in the conduction band has been excited from the valence band, leaving a hole there so that

$$n_i = p_i,$$

where the suffix indicates that we are discussing the intrinsic material. With this additional condition we can solve for E_F, which is found to be

$$E_F = - E_G/2 + \frac{3kT}{4} \ln (m_h^*/m_e^*).$$

The second term is very small so that for an intrinsic semiconductor the *Fermi level* (the name given to E_F in a semiconductor) is approximately halfway between the bands.

For n- or p-type material, a different condition must be used to determine E_F; a qualitative discussion will suffice. Thus in an n-type semiconductor, n will be greater than in the intrinsic case, so that E_F must be closer to the edge of the conduction band; conversely with p-type material. In fact, the Fermi level is the only term in the expressions for n and p into which the properties of the actual specimen enter (as opposed to the properties of the particular crystal lattice, which determine E_G, N_c, N_v). Hence if we know the position of the Fermi level of a semiconductor specimen, we know whether it is n-type or p-type, and to what extent.

If now we multiply the expressions for n and p above, we have

$$np = N_c N_v \exp (- E_G/kT).$$

Note that the result is independent of E_F, so that it is true for *all* specimens of a given semiconducting material. In other words, if we take n-type germanium, then in order to maintain the constancy of the np product, p must be smaller than in the intrinsic case, and conversely for p-type material. We can speak of the holes and electrons respectively as *minority carriers*. This relation linking the thermal equilibrium concentrations of holes and electrons is of great value and importance.

It is necessary to include a warning, for the analysis we have given is restricted in its application, in that it is assumed that the electrons in the conduction band (for instance) are so few that the Pauli principle is no longer a real limitation on the occupancy of a level. In other words, the chance of more than two electrons entering the same level is a remote one that can be ignored. Understandably, this will cease to be true of an n-type material if the donor density is high enough. Semiconductors where this occurs are said to be *degenerate*, the others, *non-degenerate*. By implication, all the theoretical results we shall make use of here will refer to the non-degenerate case only. The degenerate semiconductor can be regarded as a less satisfactory idealization—its conductivity can be interpreted in terms of charged particles but these no longer obey classical statistics.

10.6 **Purification of semiconductors.** We saw in the last chapter that the basic importance of semiconductors lies in their effectiveness in providing a testing ground for a manageable theory of conductivity, and since our testing will be of an experimental nature, it is important to be sure of the conditions that must be fulfilled if useful experimental work is to be done.

It was stated in Section 9.21 that intrinsic germanium at room temperature contains one hole, and one electron, per 10^9 atoms. If there should be present in the germanium one atom of donor impurity per 10^8 atoms, a large increase in carrier concentration and conductivity would result. If, then, the properties of pure germanium are to be investigated at room temperature, we must be sure that the excess concentration of donors or acceptors is less than one part in a thousand million. This is an extraordinarily stringent requirement, calling for a degree of purity at least 1000 times better than anything previously demanded. At the outset, no chemical methods of purification were known which could achieve this, and in any case no suitable methods of analysis were available. The electrical conductivity of the semiconductor clearly provides an analytical tool of the required sensitivity, and the demand for high quality material for semiconductor devices provided an incentive to meet the problems of purification.

Of particular importance in the purification of semiconductors is a process known as *zone refining* developed for the purpose by Pfann and universally applied to germanium and silicon. The method depends on the fortunate (and purely chance) circumstances that, when liquid and solid germanium (for instance) are in equilibrium the concentration of an impurity in solution is much greater in the liquid than in the solid. If a narrow region (the 'zone') of an impure germanium ingot is melted, and, by traversing the crystal through the heat source, is passed across the crystal, the effect is to gather a high proportion of the impurities into the liquid zone, and to sweep them through the crystal where they are finally collected at one end of it and subsequently rejected. A number (often six) of zone 'passes' of this kind can be made with cumulative effect, and intrinsic germanium produced.

Silicon has a higher band gap than germanium, and a correspondingly lower intrinsic carrier density ($1 \cdot 4 \times 10^{16}/m^3$). Intrinsic material cannot yet be produced, but high resistivity material can be prepared by compensation.

10.7 **The growth of single crystals.** It need not be stressed again that all the theoretical work we have considered refers to crystals, so that a good semiconductor material must be crystalline. In itself this is not hard to achieve, but to prepare a specimen which, like a typical piece of metal, is polycrystalline, made up of small interlacing crystallites in more or less random orientation, is not sufficient.

The reason for this lies in the peculiar nature of a crystal surface. The boundary between two grains of different crystalline orientations has many properties resembling those of a free surface, and we can regard it as such. Now atoms near the surface of a crystal will not have the regular environment of those deep in the interior. The forces exerted on them by their neighbours will not be symmetrical, with the result that the atoms will take up slightly abnormal equilibrium positions. These disturbances will alter the nature of the energy bands near a surface, often causing localized levels ('surface states') to split off. It is not necessary to go into further detail to see that, near a surface, the properties of the crystal will be abnormal.

Chemical purity therefore is not enough, and we must reduce to a minimum the effect of surfaces; this we can do by working with *single crystals* with no internal surfaces. A single crystal can be grown by melting zone-refined germanium in a silica crucible in an inert atmosphere, and dipping into the melt a cooled 'seed' crystal. If the temperature of the melt is slightly reduced, solid germanium will be deposited on the seed crystal, and, if precautions are taken, the new growth will follow the orientation of the seed. If the growing seed is slowly withdrawn from the melt, single crystals up to several kilograms in weight can be grown without great difficulty. A similar technique can be used for other semiconducting materials.

The abnormality of a real crystal surface provides the explanation as to why, in discussing the theory of energy bands, we sought to avoid meeting one, by using the rather artificial device of cyclic boundary conditions (see especially Section 9.9). Our crystal was seen as one unit in a regular stack of identical 'bricks', forming an infinite aggregate with no surfaces, but having the analytically valuable property of periodicity in the dimensions of the original crystal.

10.8 Experimental determination of semiconductor parameters.
We mentioned in Section 10.3 that the parameters describing the behaviour of a semiconductor crystal have to be determined experimentally. We must discuss this in slightly greater detail.

(i) *Determination of conductivity*. For an intrinsic semiconductor $\sigma = e\,(n\mu_e + p\mu_h)$ (which follows from a generalization of the argument in Section 9.2) but for an extrinsic specimen $n \gg p$ or $p \gg n$ so one of the terms can be neglected. Even then, there are two unknowns, n and μ_e for the case of n-type material. We need a separate means of measuring one of these. It is important that resistance associated with contacts is eliminated. To do this, a sample in the form of a rod of specified dimensions is used; current is supplied through large-area contacts

K

at the ends (Fig. 10.3), but the potential drop is across between a second pair of contacts between the current leads. This potential difference is measured with an electrometer of very high impedance, or potentiometrically, so that no appreciable current flows through the voltage probes, and so contact resistances there are unimportant. As an alternative to the fabrication of a shaped specimen, four collinear probes can be applied to a flat surface on a semi-infinite slab of semiconductor (dimensions large compared with probe spacing), a method more suitable for the rapid testing of material as a production check, for instance.

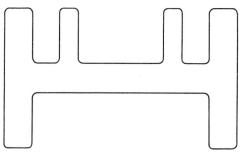

FIG. 10.3   Shaped specimen for conductivity measurement. The projections at the end enable large area (low resistance) current connections to be made, and the inner projections serve the same purpose for the voltage leads.

(ii) *Hall effect.* Electrons flowing through a crystal under an applied potential difference will be deflected by a magnetic field, as will free electrons. This suggests a 'piling up' of charge at the sides of the specimen, and equilibrium will be established when the voltage developed in this way (the Hall voltage) just balances the deflecting effect of the magnetic field (Fig. 10.4). Experiment shows that the Hall field F_H is proportional to the current density $\mathcal{J}$ through the specimen, and to the magnetic field. The constant of proportionality is called the *Hall constant R.* The Hall field, F_H, is

$$F_H = R \, \mathcal{J} \, B_y$$

The force on a single electron with velocity v under the crossed fields F_H and B_y is

$$e(F_H + v \, B_y).$$

In the absence of an external force

$$F_H = - \, v \, B_y = - \, \mu_e F_z \, B_y,$$

but

$$\mathcal{J} = n e \mu_e F_z,$$

so

$$F_H = \left(\frac{1}{ne}\right) \mathcal{J} \, B_y \text{ or } R = 1/ne.$$

Hence, knowing R, we can determine the carrier concentration directly, and also identify the carrier type, since the sign of the Hall effect determines whether we are dealing with holes or electrons, under given circumstances.

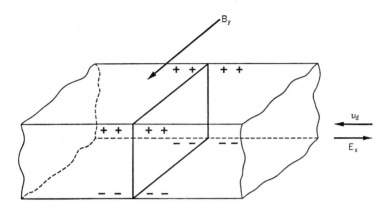

FIG. 10.4   Hall effect in a specimen of n-type semiconductor of rectangular cross section. The direction of magnetic field, electric field, and electron drift velocity are shown, and the ensuing tendency to charge separation is indicated.

Combined measurement of the Hall constant and conductivity enables both the majority carrier density and mobility to be determined (the situation is more complicated in intrinsic material). These are the most important quantities in semiconductor work. Quantities like the electron and hole effective masses, and the band gap, are determined by the crystal lattice, and are the same for all germanium specimens (for instance) and can be determined on a 'once for all' basis, reference being made subsequently to tables for the results. On the other hand, the majority carrier concentration of a specimen is peculiar to it, since it is determined by the impurity content. Mobility is a property of the crystal lattice, so long as the dominent scattering process is due to lattice (thermal) scattering. If the impurity content is high, and the temperature low, then the mobility may be determined by impurity scattering, and it will then be a characteristic of that specimen alone.

REFERENCES

SHEPHERD, A. A. *An Introduction to the Theory and Practice of Semiconductors*, Constable, London (1958).

PROBLEMS

	Germanium	Silicon
Atomic weight	72·6	28·9
Density, kg/m³	5·46 × 10³	2·42 × 10³
Electron mobility, m²/volt sec	0·36	0·12
Hole mobility, m²/volt sec	0·17	0·05

10.1 What concentration of donors will be required for the electron density in the conduction band to be ten times greater than that of the intrinsic material at 300°K in (i) germanium, (ii) silicon?

For germanium $np = 3·10 \times 10^{32} T^3 \exp(-0·785/kT)$

For silicon $np = 1·5 \times 10^{33} T^3 \exp(-1·21/kT)$

10.2 Calculate the drift velocity of electrons in germanium in a field of 10^2 volt/m, and in a field of 10^4 volt/m. Compare the figures with the velocity of the random thermal motion of electrons in germanium.

10.3 Because the electron and hole mobilities in silicon are different, the lowest possible conductivity in the material does not correspond to the intrinsic condition. Calculate the value of the minimum conductivity, and state whether it corresponds to n- or p-type material. Calculate also the conductivity of intrinsic silicon.

10.4 The following data refer to the conductivity of a semiconductor at the temperatures given. The same values are found for all specimens examined, within experimental error. Show how a knowledge of the mobilities of both carriers at the appropriate temperatures is necessary to derive the data in the third column.

Conductivity (mho/m)	Temperature (°K)	np (m^{-6})
1·5.10⁴	833	2·1.10³⁰
3·0.10³	625	2·0.10²⁹
6·3.10²	500	2·2.10²⁸
1·2.10²	417	2·8.10²⁷
2·4.10¹	357	3·5.10²⁶
4·0.	313	4·6.10²⁵
7·0.10⁻¹	277	6·0.10²⁴

Derive a value of the energy gap from the data. Calculate the shortest wavelength at which the material is transparent. Evaluate the latter quantity for materials of energy gap 0·17 eV, 2·25 eV, and 3·3 eV.

10.5 A germanium rod has a cross section of 6 mm × 1 mm. Hall probes are placed on the small area sides, the specimen is placed in a magnetic field of 10^{-1} weber/m² and a current of 1 mA is passed along the length of the rod. The difference in measured Hall voltage when the magnetic field is reversed in direction is 9 mV. If the measurement is repeated with the direction of current flow reversed, the result is 8·4 mV. Account for the difference. Calculate the Hall voltage obtained when the probes are placed on the large area sides. If the conductivity of the material is 82·45 mho/m, calculate the carrier concentration and mobility. If the direction of current flow, magnetic field, and Hall field correspond respectively to the positive directions in a right-handed set of co-ordinate axes, what is the nature of the charge carrier?

Chapter 11

The p-n Junction and the Transistor

11.1 Semiconductor and vacuum electronics compared. We have seen that the electrical conductivity of a semiconductor depends on the impurities it contains, and a range of valuable applications follow directly from this. The semiconductor itself may be used as a resistive element responding to changes in light level on account of its photoconductivity (as in the selenium or cadmium sulphide photocell), or to changes of temperature which affect the equilibrium carrier density (as in the thermistor). A more valuable and extensive range of applications would be possible if the semiconductor could be operated as a nonlinear element, that is to say, if the carrier density could be directly controlled by an electrical input, rather as the space charge of a valve can be modified by a change in grid potential.

In the case of a uniform semiconductor, the process of conduction involves no real disturbance of equilibrium. The drift velocity imposed by an applied field on the random thermal motion of the carriers is a small effect, except at very high fields ($> 5 \times 10^4$ volt/m), and the disturbance of thermal equilibrium can be neglected subject to the same limitation.

Because of the generally low resistance of semiconductors there can be no question of building up a space charge of injected electrons or holes, since the internal electric fields which would result could only be sustained by prohibitively large current flow. This is in marked contrast to the situation in vacuum electronics. A material with a wide band gap, if sufficiently pure or highly compensated, approximates more closely to insulating behaviour at room temperature; in this case, space charge effects similar to those encountered in a vacuum seem to occur. Attempts to exploit them in a 'solid state triode' are still in their early stages.

11.2 Contact phenomena—the p-n junction. The thermal equilibrium conditions sufficient to describe low field conductivity in semiconductors (in terms of a slow drift superposed upon the random thermal motion), clearly cannot obtain close to the contacts which link the semiconductor with an external circuit. The effective carrier density in a metal is greater than that in a semiconductor; when a current flows a new equilibrium must be brought about in the surface region of the crystal beneath the contact. The whole question of contacts to semiconductors is one of considerable interest. Highly nonlinear behaviour is usual, and the 'cat's-whisker' detector of the heroic age of radio reception depends on these properties of a semiconductor—metal contact.

Semiconductor contacts, then, are worth examining. Our original interest in semiconductors was aroused by a more general concern with electronic conduction in crystals. We then found that metal crystals were too complicated in this respect, and turned to the study of semiconductors instead. In the same way, we should find the study of a metal-to-semiconductor contact unrewarding; instead we shall investigate the contact between different regions within a single semiconductor crystal—to be more specific, the junction between a p-type and an n-type material, referred to simply as a p-n junction.

Our reason for doing so can be justified by highly practical results. The wide-ranging success of the junction transistor is based on a clear understanding of at least the principles of the mechanism of a p-n junction; it is this understanding which has enabled junctions to be designed for specific applications, for instance the junction transistor. In addition, there is a *point contact* transistor, but its evolution and improvement were held up for lack of knowledge. Its importance is therefore purely historical.

In discussing the p-n junction, we specifically mentioned 'contact between two regions *within a single semiconductor crystal*'. Merely to place for instance a crystal of p-type germanium in contact with one of n-type germanium is not by any means the same thing, for the behaviour of the junction would be dominated by the 'surface states' (Section 10.7) of the free surfaces in contact, and would exhibit none of the interesting and valuable properties to be discussed in the following sections.

A simple condition can be stated describing the equilibrium of a semiconductor in contact with a metal or with another semiconductor; the Fermi levels must coincide for the two regions. We have encountered the Fermi level as a constant in the Fermi-Dirac distribution function (Section 10.5), but since the statistics of occupancy of energy levels is a subject closely related to thermodynamics, it is not surprising that when we investigate the physical meaning of E_F it is found to be the *chemical potential* of the electrons. Equality of chemical potentials is a very general criterion for equilibrium between different systems, and what we have just stated is a special case of this.

11.3 **Equilibrium in the p-n junction—static approach.** Applying this to a p-n junction, and taking the case of germanium as an example, the equilibrium situation is as shown in Fig. 11.1. To satisfy the equilibrium condition, the bands must be bent as in the figure. Now a band edge which is not horizontal implies a change in carrier energy with position in the band, i.e. an electric field. We can see in another way that the region of sloping bands represents an electric field. To the right of the junction, the density of electrons is very high, to the left it is very low, and conversely in the case of holes. Since the electrons and holes are in random motion, and continually experiencing collisions, there is a net motion across the boundary; this can be seen by considering a unit area at the boundary and parallel to it, and computing the number of impacts on it. More electrons strike this boundary from the right than from the left, because of the disparity of electron density on the two sides; in the case of holes the opposite is true. This process, well known in non-uniform gases, and common to all collections of particles in random motion, is *diffusion* (Section 3.10).

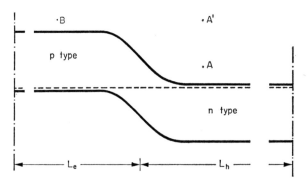

FIG. 11.1   Equilibrium at a p-n junction. The Fermi level is shown dotted. The breaks in the bands near the edges of the diagram indicate distortion of the scale—in fact the diffusion lengths L_e, L_h, are very much longer than the transition region where the curvature of the bands occurs.

Diffusion alone would equalize the carrier concentrations across the boundary; in this case however it is opposed by an electrical force. For the diffusion, as soon as it begins, tends to leave the n-region with a positive charge, and the p-region with a negative, an unbalance which soon prevents further diffusion. This charge is confined to the region of the boundary; in the n-type material it consists of donors, in the p-type material, acceptors. In each case this is a space charge of ionized impurities, at the fixed lattice sites where the impurities are substituted. This is the only kind of space charge we can expect to find in a semiconductor. As Poisson's equation indicates, it will be associated with a field, in agreement with the earlier interpretation of the bent bands. The region over which the field extends is known as the *transition region*; its extent, and its distribution about the boundary (not usually symmetrical), depends on the impurity concentrations in the n and p-type material, so that one has an element of control over the configuration when designing a junction.

The extent of the displacement of either band in completely traversing the transition region is known as the *built-in potential*. This potential cannot be measured with a voltmeter since it can be shown that a voltmeter indicates differences of Fermi level, and in equilibrium there can be no such differences. If an external potential is applied to the junction, the equilibrium is disturbed, and the transition region will adjust itself, by further ionization or recombination of donors and acceptors, until the applied potential is just taken up by the space charge. This involves changes in the thickness of the transition region, and of the field distribution in it. It is possible to look at this in another way, for within the transition region there can be no permanent population of carriers—the field will sweep them out. Hence the resistance of the transition region will be much higher than that of the remainder of the crystal, so that any applied potential difference will naturally appear across the transition region. This approach fails to emphasize the change in thickness of the region, but it does stress one important thing—the transition region of a p-n junction is a good model of a perfect insulator, and its behaviour is worth studying from this point of view.

We have so far stressed only the incidental consequences of applying a potential difference to a p-n junction. The most important effect is the electric current which will flow, and this will now be discussed.

11.4   Equilibrium in the p-n junction—dynamic approach.

The account of the equilibrium in a p-n junction and the disturbance of it was couched in completely static terms. It is far more enlightening to remember that it is a dynamic matter, and that carrier density is a statistically determined quantity whose average is constant, representing an overall balance between the rate of production of carriers, and their subsequent annihilation by recombination (after, on average, the *lifetime*). This means that equilibrium at a p-n junction is to be thought of in terms of equal and opposite currents of electrons, and equal and opposite currents of holes, across the boundary, rather than a state of separate equilibrium on each side of it, with no physical link between.

Turning to Fig. 11.1, an electron in the n-region near the boundary, whose energy is represented by the point A, will not be able to enter the p-region, but an electron at A′ will be able to do so, and a proportion of the electrons with energy E_A' or greater will reach B in the course of their random thermal wandering through the lattice. The ratio N_A'/N_A, where respectively N_A', N_A are the densities of electrons having energies E_A', E_A corresponding to A′, A is given by

$$\frac{N'_A}{N_A} = \exp\left(\frac{-(E_A' - E_A)}{kT}\right),$$

a result which will be useful later (Section 11.6). There will not be a significant reverse flow of this kind from B to A′ because the electron density at B is that appropriate to a p-type material, and is therefore very small compared with that at A′.

The reverse current of electrons which brings about the equilibrium arises in a different way. In the p-type material, as in any semiconductor, hole and electron pairs are constantly being generated by the interchange of thermal energy between lattice vibrations and the electrons. The reverse process restores energy to the lattice when the electron and hole recombine, and the energy E_G is restored to the lattice. Normally, a newly created electron in a p-type material will survive for a certain time, whose averaged value we can call the *lifetime*, and will then be annihilated by recombination. If, on the other hand, the electron is produced near the edge of the transition region, the chances are that its thermal motion during this lifetime will carry it over the brink, into the transition region, whereupon it will be able to occupy a state of lower potential energy by descending the potential hill represented by the transition region. The limited lifetime of these electrons means that the 'collecting ground' for electrons that have any chance at all of reaching the transition region, will also be limited in extent. This is represented in practice by delimiting a region of the p-type material, within a distance L_e from the start of the transition region, such that all electrons within this distance will be 'collected' by the n-region. L_e is the *diffusion length* for electrons. We can represent the equilibrium as far as electrons are concerned by the symbolic statement

$$\mathcal{J}_d = \mathcal{J}_t,$$

where $\mathcal{J}_d$ is the n-p electron current density due to diffusion, and $\mathcal{J}_t$ is the p-n electron current density due to thermal generation.

The equilibrium of holes at the junction can be handled in a similar way. The only new feature met with in this case concerns the fact that the energy scale of the conventional diagram shows hole potential energy increasing *downwards*, because of the relationship of electrons and holes. This has the paradoxical consequence that holes appear to 'roll uphill' in the transition region.

11.5   **Analysis of the p-n junction—the assumptions.**   This treatment of dynamic equilibrium contains a number of concealed assumptions, for instance that all the applied voltage appears across the transition region, which can never be *quite* true. Less trivial is the assumption that the thickness of the transition region is small compared with the diffusion lengths of the carriers, which means that we can neglect any carrier recombination and generation in the transition region. We are also restricted, when current is passing, to currents small enough for us to be able to neglect any space due to charge 'in transit' compared with the fixed space charge due to ionized impurities.

It does not follow that all practical p-n junctions, under all attainable conditions, will satisfy these assumptions. Most real p-n junctions will deviate from the ideal behaviour in one way or another. For instance no silicon p-n junction has the current characteristics we shall derive in the next section, most probably because recombination in the junction is always important. It is sufficient if some p-n junctions can be made which behave in the way the simple theory indicates, and this is certainly true for germanium. Beyond this, it is enough that we should be able to interpret the behaviour of less tractable junctions in terms of deviations from this ideal state, and this can in fact be done with an encouraging measure of success. For a more detailed discussion of the theory of the p-n junction when the simple assumptions fail, see Jonscher's book referred to at the end of the chapter.

11.6 The p-n junction under applied voltage.

When a voltage is applied to a p-n junction, what current flows? As mentioned in Section 11.3, the Fermi level will be displaced on crossing the transition region (it is not defined within it). If the n-region is made positive with respect to the p-, the height of the barrier to the diffusion current will increase; as it does so, the number of electrons able to diffuse will decrease exponentially, following the decrease in the distribution function with increasing energy. The thermally generated current, on the other hand, will be completely unchanged. As the applied voltage increases from zero, therefore, the balance between the two is increasingly upset by the diminution of the diffusion current, until this is negligible; thus the net current flowing increases with the voltage applied, until it is effectively equal to the thermally generated component alone, a constant 'saturation' current, independent of voltage.

If, on the other hand, the n-region is made negative with respect to the p-, the diffusion current will increase very rapidly as more and more electrons can diffuse, and again the thermally generated current is unchanged; hence in this direction the current rises rapidly with bias.

The hole contributions in the two cases are closely similar in their behaviour, and the sum of the two gives the variation of total current with bias in each direction.

This argument can readily be extended into a crudely quantitative form, as follows.

Consider first the electron contribution. The net current density is given by

$$\mathscr{J}_e = \mathscr{J}_{de} - \mathscr{J}_{te}$$

(by an extension of the notation used earlier). Now $\mathcal{J}_{de}$ depends on the number of electrons able to diffuse over the potential barrier, and from the result of Section 11.4, this will be of the form exp (eV/kT) where V is the applied voltage.

$$\mathcal{J}_{de} = C \exp (eV/kT).$$

C is a constant which we can determine by considering the situation when $V = 0$. When $V = 0$, $\mathcal{J}_e = 0$ and $\mathcal{J}_{de} = \mathcal{J}_{te} = C$; hence in general

$$\mathcal{J}_e = \mathcal{J}_{te} [\exp (eV/kT) - 1].$$

We must now calculate the magnitude of $\mathcal{J}_{te}$.

The equilibrium concentration of electrons in the p-region is n_p. If the lifetime of these minority carriers is τ_e, then, on average, the equilibrium population will be sustained if n_p/τ_e new electrons are produced per second on the p-type side of the junction, for unit volume.

Now if we consider a junction of unit area, those electrons produced within a distance L_e of the junction will be collected, where L_e is the appropriate diffusion length. The current due to these is

$$\mathcal{J}_{te} = \frac{eL_e n_p}{\tau_e}.$$

Similarly we have for holes

$$\mathcal{J}_{th} = \frac{eL_h p_n}{\tau_h},$$

and summing the two contributions

$$\mathcal{J} = e \left(\frac{L_e n_p}{\tau_e} + \frac{L_h p_n}{\tau_h} \right) \left(\exp \left(\frac{eV}{kT} \right) - 1 \right).$$

The form of these current characteristics is shown in Fig. 11.2. p-n junctions can be made from germanium which follow the predicted behaviour very closely.

The unsymmetrical characteristics are very similar to those of an ideal rectifier, and a p-n junction, or *junction diode*, has many practical applications in electronic circuits on this account. The behaviour of the junction diode as a rectifier is subject to important limitations. These are not revealed by the simple theory and will now be described.

11.7   **Breakdown at a p-n junction.**   First, there is the behaviour at high inverse voltages. In these conditions the field in the transition region becomes very large. Electrons moving in a high field (the same is true of holes) no longer move with a drift velocity proportional to the field. They gain energy from the field faster than they can lose it to the crystal lattice

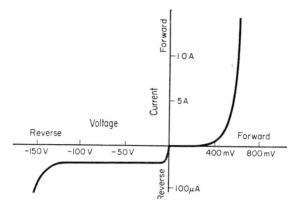

FIG. 11.2   Current-voltage curves for a germanium p-n junction, showing rectifying action—note the change of scale between the forward and reverse regions. The onset of avalanche breakdown is shown.

by collision, and are no longer even approximately in thermal equilibrium with the lattice. For this reason they are often referred to as 'hot' electrons. This process can continue until another, more efficient way of losing energy becomes available, and this will occur when the electron has enough energy to create a hole and electron pair. Both the hole and the electron produced in this way can themselves be accelerated by the field, and produce carrier pairs themselves. There is, in fact, opportunity for an indefinitely increasing avalanche of carriers, giving a 'breakdown' analogous to the Townsend process in a gas (Section 7.9). The voltage at which this breakdown occurs can be controlled by adjustment of the impurity content on each side of the junction, (roughly, the higher the impurity content the lower the breakdown voltage) and its form, i.e. whether the current rises abruptly to breakdown from its saturation current ('hard' characteristic), or gradually increases over a range of voltage below breakdown ('soft' characteristic), can be controlled by the method of manufacture.

The breakdown of a reverse biased diode is useful as a voltage reference —the *Zener diode*—with the advantage just mentioned that the breakdown voltage can be chosen anywhere within a wide range (in contrast to the neon tube, Section 7.17). If, on the other hand, the diode is required to rectify a high voltage, the breakdown is the principal limitation of performance and must be made as high as possible. Silicon diodes made by diffusion (Section 11.19) are commercially available with breakdown voltages of several hundred volts.

11.8   **High frequency behaviour of a p-n junction.**   The second limitation of the simple theory we wish to consider is the behaviour at high frequencies, as in the application of the diodes to the detection of radio waves. For this purpose, the capacity of the rectifier is important, for if it is too high its effect is that of a shunt across the rectifier. There are two processes which make the capacity of a junction diode rather high.

(i) *Transition layer capacitance.* As discussed in Section 11.3, the application of a voltage to a p-n junction changes the width of, and the total space charge in, the transition region. This process resembles the charging of a condenser, but a non-linear condenser, whose plate separation depends on the voltage across it, in fact.

(ii) *Hole storage capacitance.* In one half cycle of the a.c., the diode will be biased in the low resistance (forward) direction, and then a stream of positive holes will be injected into the n-region. (Depending on conditions, see Section 11.11, electrons may instead be injected into the p-region, or both may occur simultaneously. The argument is not affected by these complications, so we will consider the 'hole' case.) In the ensuing half-cycle, successful rectification depends on the current falling at once to the saturation value. It will not do this, because the holes stored in the n-region will be swept out, increasing the effective saturation current. This can be avoided if the holes recombine with electrons in the n-region in a time that is short compared with the half cycle. The 'hole lifetime' cannot be reduced indefinitely without an adverse effect on the rectifying characteristics, so this sets an upper limit on the frequency that can be usefully rectified. This can be expressed in terms of a shunting 'hole storage capacitance'. Typical values of hole storage times are 10^{-4} sec and the corresponding value of the storage capacitance is ~ 100 pF, which is likely to be considerably larger than the contribution due to (i).

These capacitances prevent the use of junction diodes at high frequencies. Ironically enough, in the detection of microwaves, for which of course the junction diode is useless, the cat's-whisker in slightly refined form continues to reign supreme.

These sources of capacity are not without compensating advantages. The non-linear transition layer capacity can be exploited in parametric amplification; this is outside our scope but is discussed in Reference 4 at the end of the chapter.

11.9   The reverse-biased diode as a detector of minority carriers.
The hole storage effects point the way to a number of useful applications of the diode which we have not so far considered. Hole storage indicates that the back current of a diode can provide an indication of sources of carriers other than thermal generation. In hole storage these effects are purely transient, but a diode with a d.c. bias will show an enhanced

saturation current if excess carriers are being generated by light falling on
the crystal; this can be the basis of a useful photoconductive device, the
photodiode or the *phototransistor*. Light falling on a p-n junction will shift
the Fermi levels, and consequently change the built-in potential of the
junction. This change represents an e.m.f., a *photo-e.m.f.*, by which light
can cause a current to flow in a circuit, and which provides a means for the
direct conversion of light to electrical energy. These photovoltaic cells or
solar batteries are an essential source of power in artificial satellites. A
humbler but more familiar example is the photographic light meter, which
makes use of the photovoltaic effect in a junction in the semiconductor
selenium, a structure more complex than a p-n junction but of similar
properties. Perhaps the most important use of the reverse biased diode as
a detector of carriers is in the collector junction of the transistor. This will
be considered in Section 11.13.

11.10 **The tunnel diode.**   One of the most striking ways in which
the quantum and classical approaches to physics differ is shown in the
consideration of two electron energy levels, A and B, of the same energy
but separated by a potential barrier of finite height. On classical principles,
there is no possibility of an electron initially at A ever reaching B, but

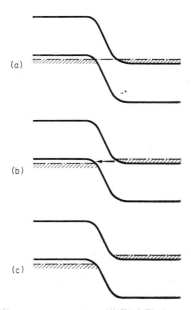

Fig. 11.3   Energy levels in the tunnel diode:
(a) No bias.
(b) Small forward bias—tunnelling can occur (as shown by arrow).
(c) Larger forward bias—no tunnelling.

according to wave mechanical principles, there is a finite chance—depending on the barrier shape, and only appreciable when the barrier is thin—that the electron might 'tunnel' through to B.

This principle, responsible for occurrences as diverse as the alpha-particle emission of some radioactive nuclei, and the emission of electrons from metal surfaces by the action of high electric fields alone (Section 7.18), produces a striking effect in suitably made p-n junctions. It is necessary to make a p-n junction with really high densities of both acceptor and donor impurities. If this is done, the semiconductor is more like a metal, the Fermi levels are within the bands, and the equilibrium state of the junction is as shown in Fig. 11.3(a). Another consequence of the high impurity density is to produce a very narrow transition region. This arises because the ionized impurity atoms are close together, and so produce a high space charge density; hence the equilibrium difference in potential is built up in a very short distance. Consider the effect of a small forward bias, Fig. 11.3(b). The bias brings to the same horizontal level empty and full states in the valence and conduction bands respectively, separated by only a very thin (100 Å) transition region. The conditions for tunnelling are satisfied, and an enhanced forward current, the tunnel current, is observed (Fig. 11.4). It rises to a maximum when the overlap of the bands is a maximum, and then decreases as the overlap diminishes once more (Fig. 11.3(c)). Since the latter decrease is brought about by a further increase in forward bias, it corresponds to 'negative resistance' behaviour and is essentially unstable, and in practice one observes a sudden jump from a high current state to a low current state (A to B on Fig. 11.4). The speed of this jump is very high ($\sim 10^{-10}$ sec) so the tunnel diode acts as a high speed switch, between its two conduction states. As such it has potentialities as an element in rapid logic circuits for digital computation.

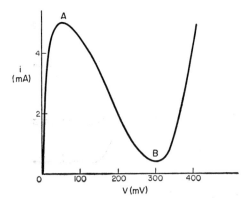

FIG. 11.4   Forward characteristic of tunnel diode.

11.11   **Injection ratio of a p-n junction.**   Their remains one further important property of the p-n junction to consider. In calculating the current characteristics of the junction, we assessed the contribution of holes and electrons separately, and added them. We shall now concern ourselves with the relative sizes of these contributions. That factor in each contribution which depends on voltage is the same for each, so it will suffice to look at the saturation currents for this purpose. We shall calculate the quantity

$$\gamma = I_h/(I_e + I_h)$$

which is known as the *injection ratio*, and defined as the fraction of the total current carried by holes.

Using the expression for the saturation currents due to electrons and holes (Section 11.6), we have

$$\gamma = \frac{L_h p_n/\tau_h}{L_h p_n/\tau_h + L_e n_p/\tau_e},$$

and by a little algebra this can be transformed to

$$\gamma = [1 + (\rho_p L_h/\rho_n L_e)]^{-1}$$

where ρ_p and ρ_n are the resistivities of the p- and n-type materials respectively, and L_h, L_e the diffusion lengths for holes and electrons in the n- and p-type materials respectively.

From this we see the important result that, if a p-n junction is made with a highly doped p-region (low resistivity) and a lightly doped n-region, the current through it will be almost entirely in the form of holes.

In the particular case of the junction forward biased, the current—which can be large—takes the form almost entirely of holes flowing into the n-region, and grossly disturbs the thermal equilibrium there. This is described as *minority carrier injection*.

We have in this way achieved our aim of disturbing the equilibrium distribution of carriers in a semiconductor by electrical means (the injecting current). The very large changes in hole concentration which we can produce in this way are, it is important to note, achieved *without accumulating a space charge*, because electrons in the conduction band, being even more numerous than the injected carriers, will be able to move to maintain local electrical neutrality all the time. The disturbance will therefore increase the local electron density, and clearly the effect of the injection will be to change the conductivity of the material locally. It is all possible because there are two species of carrier in a semiconductor.

11.12   **Carrier diffusion.**   Before dealing with the application of the

L

foregoing to the junction transistor, a word should be said about the life history of a cloud of positive holes injected into n-type material in the way described. First of all, because we have an inhomogeneous distribution of the holes in space, *diffusion* will occur. The rate at which particles flow by diffusion—whatever their nature—is given by the diffusion law

$$\frac{\partial n}{\partial t} = - D \frac{\partial n}{\partial x},$$

where D is the diffusion constant.

The diffusion constant for the holes cannot easily be calculated theoretically, but it can be measured experimentally. On the other hand, both the diffusion constant and the mobility are consequences of the essentially random, collision-determined nature of carrier motion in the crystal, and a relation between the two was derived by Einstein:

$$D = \frac{kT}{e} \mu.$$

Hence, if we have measured the mobility as discussed in Section 10.8, there is no need to measure D separately.

In studying motion of the holes under diffusion, we virtually ignore the fact that the holes are charged particles and this is because, as mentioned above, the electrons, as majority carriers, can move unobtrusively to preserve neutrality. If the number of electrons is not much greater than the number of holes, as the limiting case of intrinsic material is approached, the need for this continual adjustment will be more keenly felt, and the diffusion constant will be reduced—this is called '*ambipolar diffusion*',

The holes are not free to distribute themselves at leisure by diffusion. Their life is literally too short, for they will continually be removed by recombination with electrons. We can define an average lifetime for the holes. The lifetime is certainly a property that will be different for each crystal, and it may well be found to be different for different injected hole concentrations, and is most unlikely to be the same as the 'lifetime' defined in Section 11.4. So long as we are concerned only with orders of magnitude, we can ignore the effects that stem from the complicated kinetics of recombination—like chemical reactions in the crystal—and speak boldly about 'lifetime' with deliberate ambiguity, remembering that its value will vary widely from crystal to crystal. Typical values for germanium range from 10^{-4} sec downwards; the more perfect the crystal, the longer the lifetime.

The hole can diffuse only a certain distance in its lifetime, a distance which can be calculated, and is in fact $\sqrt{D_h \tau_h}$ in the simple case of one-dimensional motion. This is identical with the diffusion length L_h introduced in Section 11.4, so that we now know how this quantity can be determined in terms of basic quantities, in which category we must now place lifetime.

The lifetime can be measured, at least roughly, by exciting a pulse of photocurrent in the crystal using a spark or flash tube as a source, and measuring the time constant of the exponential decay oscillographically.

It is possible to write down formal equations describing the change in carrier densities in space and time due to drift in an electric field, diffusion and recombination. The results we have obtained for the characteristics of the p-n junction can be calculated rigorously in this way. We shall not dwell on the calculation—the method we have given reveals more about the physics of the process—but the complete calculation does provide a firm basis for improving and refining the theory, in a way which the simpler one does not. Interested readers are referred to the references at the end of the chapter, and especially to Shockley's classic but difficult original paper on the p-n junction (Reference 5 at the end of the chapter).

11.13   **The junction transistor.**   As was mentioned in Section 11.11, a forward biased p-n junction can be used to disturb the equilibrium carrier concentrations in, say, the n-type material at one side of the junction, in response to an electrical input. In Section 11.9 it was stated that the saturation current of a reverse biased p-n junction is sensitive to such disturbances. Now suppose we have a configuration of two plane parallel p-n junctions in a single crystal, giving a p-n-p sequence of conductivity types. Then if, say, the left hand junction is forward biased, it will inject holes into the central n-region (the *base*) and is referred to as the *emitter*. Provided that the thickness of the base is comparable with or less than the diffusion length, a proportion of the injected holes will reach the right-hand junction. If this junction is backward biased, it will act as a *collector* of the injected holes. The arrangement is a *p-n-p junction transistor* (Fig. 11.5). One can just as easily consider the n-p-n configuration,

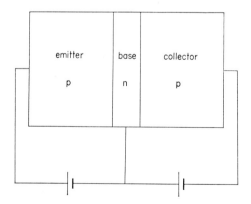

Fig. 11.5   The p-n-p junction transistor. Common base connection.

which will be equally effective, but it will be sufficient to describe one of these alternatives. It is important to note that the holes cross the base region by diffusion; there is generally no electric field in the base.

11.14 Charge control in the transistor. In describing the triode valve, we regarded the charge on the grid as the immediate means of controlling the space charge current. In a somewhat similar way, in the junction transistor the charge on the base is the determining factor. If the base is charged to a given (negative) potential with respect to the emitter, the height of the emitter barrier is decreased, and excess holes will be injected to bring about the neutrality of the base. There will then be a concentration gradient across the base, which will impel hole flow by diffusion from the emitter to the collector. Under perfect conditions, the flow will continue indefinitely. In practice this is prevented by two circumstances. First, the emitter current is not entirely a hole current, and its electron component depletes the charge on the base. Second, electrons are also removed from the base by recombination with the injected holes. For these reasons, a static charge on the base will not suffice, and we must supply a small but continuous current to the base, so that it is possible, and indeed usual, to regard the junction transistor as a current-operated device. The point of view just given seems to be useful for integrating the small-signal theory with the large, but we shall not pursue this topic here.

11.15 Requirements for transistor design. The problem of transistor design is twofold; to make the injection ratio at the emitter as high as possible, and to make recombination in the base as low as possible. Success in these respects is represented by the factor a_{CE}, the current amplification from emitter to collector. It should be in the region of 98 per cent. Note that the current gain in the configuration we have described is never greater than one (disregarding the restricted case where the collector bias is high enough to cause avalanche multiplication). In spite of this, power gain can result because the holes are being transferred by diffusion from a low resistance circuit (the emitter junction is forward biased) to a high resistance circuit (the collector junction is back biased). As an amplifier, the transistor has obvious advantages over the vacuum triode—extremely small size, no need to dissipate heat in the production of charge carriers, and no need for bulky auxiliary power supplies. The limitations of the transistor will be discussed next.

Before doing so, it should be pointed out that an alternative circuit arrangement for the transistor can be used which will give current gain. This is the *common emitter* configuration, as opposed to the *common base* configuration previously described, and it is shown in Fig. 11.6. If a_{CB} is the current gain in this arrangement, it can be shown that

$$a_{\mathrm{CB}} = \frac{a_{\mathrm{CE}}}{1 - a_{\mathrm{CE}}},$$

which can clearly be larger than unity. Physically, the current in the input circuit is just the small electron current arising from the imperfections of transistor action (Section 11.14); a much larger current can flow from emitter to collector.

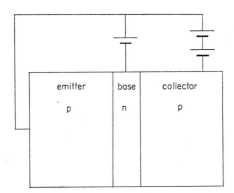

FIG. 11.6   The p-n-p junction transistor. Common emitter connection.

11.16   Operation at high power level and high frequency.

In the practical employment of the transistor we shall commonly be concerned to push its capabilities towards the attainment of a high power output, or towards operation at higher frequencies. In both directions the performance of the transistor is rather circumscribed, and we must now consider the reasons for this.

Consider first the transistor at high power levels. This requires a considerable voltage swing on the collector, and therefore a high collector reverse bias. Under this condition, avalanche breakdown of the collector may occur, and to prevent this the donor density of the base should not be too high. On the other hand, a high resistance (low donor density) in the base region is undesirable, especially at high collector bias, where there is a risk that the collector junction space charge barrier will efface the base region completely, causing a destructively high current to flow—so-called *punch through*.

Further, the large collector current means sizable heat dissipation in a very small crystal, and this will cause the collector saturation current to rise; 40°C in germanium is high enough to ruin the action of the collector. To conduct away the heat without reaching this temperature is a difficult task, and for power applications silicon is preferred, which because of its higher band gap can still operate up to 100°C.

We must now consider high frequency operation. Diffusion is an inherently slow process, so that the transit time between emitter and collector is considerable. This would not matter if the geometry of a real transistor were truly one-dimensional, but in fact there is a spread of trajectories of different lengths, and so a spread of transit times which spoils the response at a relatively low frequency. The situation is improved by designing transistors with a very narrow base. This is primarily a problem of materials technology, but it is possible in this way to make transistors whose frequency response is good up to hundreds of megacycles.

11.17 Equivalent circuits of the transistor. It is sometimes useful to consider equivalent circuits of the transistor. At its simplest we have a current generator associated with the collector resistance and capacity, the emitter resistance (and at high frequencies its capacity) and the base resistance. The last is particularly important because connection to the base region has necessarily to be physically removed from the active part of the base region. Since its distance from different parts of the active region is different, it is strictly necessary to consider these parameters as distributed rather than lumped. The base resistance is found to introduce feedback between the emitter and collector. Further complications follow from the modulation of the base width of the transistor as the collector voltage fluctuates, which provides a further source of feedback. The reader is referred to more detailed books for an account of these important matters.

11.18 Requirements for transistor materials. What is the ideal material for a transistor? A high band gap is desirable, and a large mobility (hence diffusion rate, through the Einstein relation) for at least one carrier. The material has to be tractable in the sense of allowing adequate purification and fabrication on an economic basis. Silicon and germanium are the only materials in common use, but gallium arsenide (with a wider band gap than silicon, and a higher electron mobility) may be important in the future.

11.19 Transistor manufacture. The p-n junctions in the transistor or diode may be grown into the crystal by the addition of suitable material during crystal growth, but it is the usual practice nowadays to form the junction after the preparation of a single crystal of suitable size. This can be done by forming a molten region of heavily doped semiconductor alloy on the surface and allowing it to resolidify (the alloy junction) or by allowing the required impurities to enter the crystal by diffusion, the latter being the more exacting but susceptible to more complete control. Finally, layers of semiconductor can be deposited in the correct orientation on a single crystal substrate by chemical reaction *in situ*—the so-called epitaxial growth. Most transistors and semiconductor devices include junctions made by one of these processes, or a combination of them.

REFERENCES

1. DEWITT, D. and ROSSOFF, A. L. *Transistor Electronics*, McGraw-Hill, New York (1957).

2. EVANS, J. *Fundamental Principles of Transistors*, Heywood, London (1957).

3. JONSCHER, A. K. *Principles of Semiconductor Device Operation*, Bell, London (1960).

4. NERGAARD, L. S. 'Nonlinear-capacitance amplifiers', *R.C.A. Rev.* **20**, 3 (1959).

5. SHOCKLEY, W. 'Theory of p-n junctions in semiconductors and p-n junction transistors', *Bell Syst. Tech. J.* **28**, 435 (1949).

6. GENTILE, S. P. *Basic Theory and Application of Tunnel Diodes*, Van Nostrand, Princeton (1962).

PROBLEMS

	Germanium	Silicon
Atomic weight	72·6	28·9
Density, kg/m³	$5·46 \times 10^3$	$2·42 \times 10^3$
Electron mobility, m²/volt sec	0·36	0·12
Hole mobility m²/volt sec	0·17	0·05

11.1 Use the one-dimensional form of Poisson's equation to find what field would be necessary to maintain a $0·01\%$ excess of electrons in an n-type semiconductor with 10^{22} electrons/m³ in the conduction band.

11.2 A germanium crystal contains an excess of donors over acceptors of 10^{22}/m³. 10^{24} holes/m³ are injected in a pulse whose length can be neglected; afterwards the conductivity drops to 2500 mho/m in 4×10^{-4} sec. What is the lifetime of the holes? If their mobility is $0·17$ m²/volt sec, what is their diffusion length?

11.3 Draw energy band diagrams for a p-n junction under forward and reverse bias, and use them to illustrate the discussion of Section 11.6.

11.4 It is said in Section 11.11 that the second equation in the section can be transformed into the third. Work this through in detail.

11.5   For a particular p-n junction whose area of cross section is 20 mm²;

$\sigma_n \ll \sigma_p = 500$ mho/m

$D_p \qquad = 5 \times 10^{-3}$ m/sec

$\tau_p \qquad = 300$ µsec

$n_i \qquad = 10^{20}$ m^{-3}

Plot the current-voltage characteristics for the junction for both senses of the applied voltage if $L_e/L_h = 10$ and $\sigma_p/\sigma_n = 12$. What is the ratio of the electron to the hole current?

11.6   The potential barrier in a p-n junction is associated with a space charge of ionized impurities. If, for instance, the p-region is very heavily doped, the thickness of the barrier on this side of the junction is negligible, and the total thickness can be equated with that of the space charge in the n-region.

Show, by solving Poisson's equation, that if the thickness is w, and v the applied voltage, then

$$V = eNdw^2/2\varepsilon$$

and that the maximum field in the junction is

$$Fm = 2V/w$$

(Hint: Choose an origin at the end of the space charge region remote from the junction. At this point $dV/dx = 0$ and $V = 0$ at $x = 0$; these are the boundary conditions.)

11.7   In the previous question, if avalanche breakdown occurs at a specific field F_a show, using the result of that question, that the breakdown voltage is

$$V = \frac{\varepsilon F_a{}^2}{2e} \, Nd$$

11.8   The p-n junction specified in Question 11.5 is the emitter in a p-n junction. If p_0 holes are injected into the base, whose thickness is w, then, provided w is considerably less than the diffusion length for the holes, the number reaching the collector is given by

$$p = p_0 \left(1 - \tfrac{1}{2} (w/L_p)^2\right)$$

What value must w have if a_{ce} is to have the value 0·98? The measured a_{ce} will be less than this—suggest reasons.

Chapter 12

Magnetic Properties of Matter

12.1 Magnetic effects of electron motion. In Chapter 2 we discussed the motion of electrons in atoms. We saw that the classical picture of an electron describing a calculable orbit about a nucleus is untenable, but that it retains a certain crude qualitative value. After all, the calculation of the equilibrium state of an electron by solving Schrödinger's equation reveals a probability distribution in space for the electron which surrounds the nucleus; it associates with the electron a certain angular momentum, and this suggests some kind of orbital motion. In the same context, we are introduced to the idea of *spin*.

Now a charge describing a closed orbit in space is equivalent to a circulating current, and as such has associated with it a magnetic field. Furthermore the electron, conceived as a charged sphere, is spinning about an axis within itself; this too gives rise to a magnetic field.

Hence magnetism does not arise from any special and rare properties of an atom or atomic group; on the contrary it is one of the most general consequences of electronic motion within the atom.

12.2 Description of magnetic properties—diamagnetism and precession. When a closed current loop experiences a changing magnetic flux, then in accordance with Lenz's law an induced e.m.f. is set up and in consequence the current flow is modified so as to oppose the original disturbance. The cumulative effect of this for all the electron orbits in a bulk specimen is known as *diamagnetism*. Before we can discuss these matters adequately, we must define some quantities to enable us to relate macroscopic measurements to the properties of individual atoms. The most important quantity here is the *intensity of magnetization* **M** (otherwise magnetic polarization) which is simply magnetic moment per unit volume. **M** is commonly found to be proportional to the external magnetic field, i.e.

$$\mathbf{M} = \chi\mu_0\mathbf{H},$$

which defines χ the *magnetic susceptibility*. The flux inside the medium is changed by the magnetic moments. We can take account of this by the relation

$$B = \mu_0 H + M$$

and $B = \mu\mu_0 H$, where $\mu = 1 + \chi$ defines the *permeability*.

The diamagnetic susceptibility is necessarily negative. It is very small ($\sim -10^{-5}$ mks/m^3), a value which can readily be calculated on the basis of a simple model, and which agrees well with experimental results. Diamagnetism is a universal property of matter, but in making this statement it is necessary to remember that, being small, it is likely to be completely masked by other magnetic effects, if these are present. There are no direct practical applications of the effect on account of its smallness.

The theory of diamagnetism will not be considered here, but one aspect of it is important. In calculating the effect of a magnetic field on an electron orbit, it is found to a first approximation that the orbit remains unchanged, except that it rotates around an axis parallel to the applied flux B with a uniform angular velocity ω given by

$$\omega = \frac{eB}{2m}.$$

The rotation of an orbit in this way is a *precession*, and this example—the *Larmor Precession*—is of fundamental importance in understanding the effect of a magnetic field on an electron. The curved path of a free electron is a particular case for an orbit of infinite radius—see Section 1.2. In this case the frequency is sometimes referred to as the *cyclotron frequency*, since magnetic deflection provides the principle of operation of the particle accelerator of that name. It is important because an electron in a crystal will be similarly affected; in this case the frequency will be $eB/2m^*$ and this provides us with a method of measuring m^*. Power will be absorbed by the electron from an electromagnetic wave in resonance with the cyclotron frequency, so that it is possible to determine the latter by *cyclotron resonance*. The importance of effective mass was discussed in Section 9.15; the cyclotron resonance experiment is the most direct of a very limited number of methods by which m^* can be measured, for either holes or electrons in semiconductors. We can regard it as a manifestation of the diamagnetism of conduction electrons in a crystal.

12.3 **Spin and orbital magnetic moment.** A single electron moving in an orbit will possess angular momentum on two counts: because of the orbital motion, and because of the electron spin. If then the resultant angular momentum is represented by G, the magnetic moment m associated with the electron will be proportional to this quantity:

$$m = \gamma\,G,$$

where $1/\gamma$ is the *gyromagnetic ratio*.

Since in quantum theory, angular momentum is quantized (Section 2.8) the magnetic moment itself will be restricted to discrete values. The natural unit of magnetic moment so defined is the *Bohr magneton*

$$\mu_0(eh/4\pi m),$$

and the actual magnetic moment will be

$$g\mu_0 \, (eh/4\pi m) \times \text{(angular momentum)},$$

where g is a constant with the value 1 in the case of orbital angular momentum, and approximately 2 in the case of spin. For an electron in an atom, the angular momentum will be a combination of orbital and spin values according to the l,s values of the electronic state; an appropriate value of g can be deduced for this case.

In the presence of an external magnetic field $\mathbf{H}_0$, the magnetic moments will precess about the direction of this field as axis, with the Larmor frequency, which we can now write as

$$\omega = - \, \gamma \, \mathbf{H}_0.$$

If now an external periodic magnetic field is applied, perpendicular to $\mathbf{H}_0$, having the same frequency ω, energy will be transferred from the field to the magnetic moments; the latter will increase their potential energy by increasing their angle with $\mathbf{H}_0$. For accessible values of $\mathbf{H}_0$ ($\sim 10^5$amp/m) the frequency ω corresponds to an electromagnetic wave in the microwave region, and a resonance experiment can be performed—*electron spin resonance*—whose immediate object is to determine the g-value. The latter is not only defined by l and s, as implied above. For an electron in a crystal the g-value is sensitive to the environment of the atom in a very detailed way, and the technique can be used to provide information about the atomic arrangement in the crystal. Transitions between levels of this kind, associated with different orientations of the magnetic moment to the applied field, form the basis for the operation of the three-level maser (Section 15.8).

12.4 **Macroscopic effects—paramagnetism.** We will now consider the macroscopic effects of the electronic magnetic moments. In the absence of an external field, the random orientation of the moments in bulk matter will be maintained by thermal motions; if now a magnetic field is applied there will be a tendency (opposed by thermal effects), for the moments to align with the field. The outcome of this will be a resultant magnetic moment per unit volume which can be shown to be

$$\mathbf{M} = \frac{\text{const.}\,\mathbf{H}_0}{T},$$

where T is the absolute temperature; or, in terms of susceptibility,

$$\chi = \frac{\text{const.}}{T}.$$

The inverse proportionality between susceptibility and temperature is observed experimentally and known as the *Curie law*. The positive magnetic susceptibility that arises in this way is *paramagnetism*.

It might be thought that paramagnetism would be a very widespread, if not universal property of matter, but this is not so. As mentioned in Section 3.2, free atoms other than rare gases are not common in nature. Now in these atoms, as well as in the stable molecules which are the normal state of matter, the electrons are so distributed that the resultant magnetic moment is zero. It follows then that the only important chemical compounds which exhibit paramagnetism are those containing atoms or ions of the transition or rare earth groups of the periodic table, where there is an incomplete electron shell within (Section 2.13).

In a typical paramagnetic material of this kind, the susceptibility at room temperature is $\sim + 10^{-3}$ mks/m^3; this is very small, and represents a total alignment with the field of only one atom in 10^9. It is possible to calculate (from the constant in the Curie law expression) the number of Bohr magnetons in each atomic moment; this can then be compared with the value predicted from the electron configuration of the atom or ion. It is found that although the Curie law is in fact widely (not universally) obeyed, the observed 'magneton numbers' do not usually agree with the calculated values when the ion is incorporated in a crystal. On the other hand, if the ion is in solution, agreement between theory and experiment is good. The ions in the crystal behave as if only the spin magnetic moments were effective. The electron orbital angular momentum is 'quenched' in this way because the shape of an electron orbit is determined by its l-value. If the orbit is 'dovetailed' into the available space in the crystal, it is more than likely that any reorientation of the orbit by the applied field will require large amounts of energy to overcome the forces of repulsion between the electron and its neighbours, and so be unable to take place.

12.5 **Magnetic saturation.** The figure just quoted for the room temperature susceptibility of a paramagnetic material shows that it is much too small to have any direct practical value. If, on the other hand, *all* the atomic moments can be aligned, the intensity of magnetization will be very large. To achieve this in the face of thermal randomization at room temperature would require unattainably large fields. At very low temperatures the condition can be observed; predictably, the intensity of magnetization ceases to be proportional to the field, and attains a constant value representing the alignment of all available moments—a condition of 'saturation'. Long before this condition is reached, however, significant departures from the Curie law are observed. These deviations are the more marked, the nearer together the magnetic ions in the specimen used. They arise from the 'internal field' of the specimen, whereby the field of neighbouring magnetic dipoles is no longer negligible by comparison with the applied field. We must then write, relating the *internal field* **H** to the applied field **H₀**,

$$\mathbf{H} = \mathbf{H_0} + \lambda\mathbf{M},$$

where λ is the *Weiss field constant*. Repetition of the analysis which led to the Curie law then produces the modified result

$$\chi = \frac{\text{const.}}{T - \theta},$$

the *Curie-Weiss law*, where θ is a constant (the *Curie temperature*). Notice that, at $T = \theta$, χ is infinite; since $\chi = M/H$, this means that M is finite at $H = 0$, i.e. in the absence of a magnetic field the specimen is spontaneously magnetized.

12.6 Ferromagnetism.   Viewed empirically, those magnetic materials which are of practical importance form a class apart, the so-called *ferromagnetics*; they are limited for practical purposes to the metals iron, cobalt and nickel (the salts of these metals are paramagnetic). Ferromagnetism has the following characteristics:

(i) The intensity of magnetization is not proportional to the field, and eventually reaches a saturation value for moderate fields at room temperature.

(ii) If the magnetization is studied in an increasing, and then in a decreasing field, the results at a given field are not the same, but are reproducible. For the full range of H values (negative as well as positive), the graph of M against H traces out a loop—the *hysteresis loop* (Fig. 12.5).

(iii) Ferromagnetics exhibit spontaneous magnetic polarization.

(iv) Above a certain temperature (the Curie temperature) these properties disappear; the material behaves as a paramagnetic with some interatomic interaction, so that the susceptibility follows the Curie-Weiss law.

12.7 Internal fields in ferromagnetics.   In view of what has been said, we might hope to explain the phenomena of ferromagnetism in terms of strong interactions between basically paramagnetic ions in a crystal lattice. This interaction can again be considered in terms of an internal field, but this time the constant multiplying M is to be regarded as quite empirical—we shall return later to the question of the nature of the inter-action (Section 12.12).

12.8 **The magnetic domain concept.** There is an immediate difficulty. The existence of an internal field of sufficient strength is inseparable from permanent spontaneous polarization; although ferromagnetic materials can exhibit this, they do not of course *necessarily* do so.

To deal with this, we may make the following postulate. A ferromagnetic is indeed always spontaneously polarized, but only in microscopic regions, or *domains*; these domains are normally so arranged that the sum of their moments over the whole specimen averages to zero, but they can be brought into alignment. On the domain theory, an unmagnetized ferromagnetic resembles a stack of bar magnets, with their north and south poles together, and perhaps with keepers at their ends.

There are two important items of experimental evidence for the existence of domains. In the first place, if magnetization is a matter of the alignment of domains, it may be expected to take place in discrete jumps. For this we have evidence in the so-called Barkhausen effect, which makes it possible to estimate the number of atomic magnets in a domain; this number is found to be in the neighbourhood of 10^{16}, representing a volume of about 10^{-6} cm^3 in the crystal for each domain.

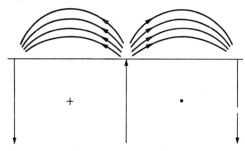

FIG. 12.1   Cross section of a ferromagnetic, showing two domains at the surface of the specimen, with opposed magnetization parallel to the surface and perpendicular to the plane of the diagram. The arrowheads on the domain boundaries represent the direction of the spin vectors at the halfway stage of their rotation through the domain wall (Fig. 12.3). The external magnetic field, concentrated near the boundaries, is due to these spins, and is shown in the diagram. (From Craik D.J. and Tebble R.S. 'Magnetic domains', in *Reports on Progress in Physics*, Vol. XXIV, Institute of Physics and the Physical Society, London (1961).)

The second item of evidence is the so-called *Bitter pattern*, obtained by applying colloidal magnetic oxide of iron to a carefully polished surface of a ferromagnetic. The magnetic particles accumulate where the magnetic field is a maximum, as do the iron filings in elementary magnetic-field-mapping experiments. In this case, the fields are high only in the boundary region between two domains (Fig. 12.1), so that the boundaries of the domains are delineated where they cut the exposed surface.

12.9 Energy balance in a domain.

Detailed study of domains shows that the structure of the domains in zero magnetic field represents the configuration of minimum potential energy for the magnetized crystal. The following are the factors which affect this energy.

(i) *Crystal direction.* It is hardly surprising that the atomic magnets are more easily aligned in some crystallographic directions than in others. There will be a natural tendency for the domain structure of a single crystal to be aligned about an 'easy' direction (Fig. 12.2).

(ii) *Magnetostatic energy.* A magnetic field **H** in free space has an energy density of $\frac{1}{2}\mu\mu_0 H^2$. If the field is that of a permanent magnet, this has to be reckoned as part of the energy of the system. The external magnetic field for the situation represented in Fig. 12.2(b) is clearly less than that of Fig. 12.2(a), and there will be less magnetostatic energy associated with it. Figure 12.2(c) has yet a smaller field, occasioned by the addition of *closure domains* perpendicular to the main ones. Where the axis of the closure domain does not correspond with a direction of easy magnetization, a configuration will be favoured in which these domains are as small as possible.

(iii) *Domain wall energy.* The boundary, or wall, between domains is known to be about 100 atoms in thickness. Now a certain amount of potential energy will be stored in the wall, because the direction of the atomic moments will gradually change on passing through it (Fig. 12.3), so that a majority will be unfavourably orientated with respect to the direction of easy magnetization. For this reason, an indefinite scaling down of individual domains, which would involve a corresponding increase in the total length of the wall, is energetically unfavourable.

  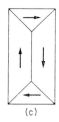

(a)   (b)   (c)

FIG. 12.2   The effect of magnetostatic energy on domain structure in a simple case. The vertical direction represents a direction of easy magnetization for the crystal considered. The extent of the external field diminishes from (a) to (c).

FIG. 12.3 A section through a domain wall. The arrows represent the orientation of the atomic magnetic moments, reversing as the wall is crossed (cf. Fig. 12.1).

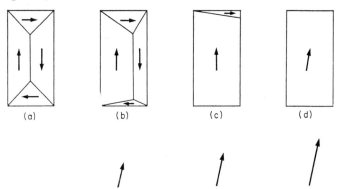

(a)   (b)   (c)   (d)

FIG. 12.4 Domain movement on magnetization. The direction and intensity of the magnetizing field is represented by the arrows below the specimens: zero in (a) and maximum in (d). Magnetization proceeds by domain wall movement in (b) and (c), and by rotation in (d).

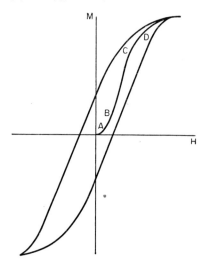

FIG. 12.5 Graph of M against H—typical hysteresis loop for a ferromagnetic. The curve ABCD describes the initial magnetization of the specimen.

12.10 **Domains and the magnetization curve.** The same kind of argument can be extended to the situation when a field is applied (Fig. 12.4). An applied field in the direction of the arrow is gradually built up from zero. Initially, magnetization takes place by the growth of favourably sited domains, at the expense of others less well placed. This process involves movements of the domain walls. Initially this domain wall movement will be reversible, and this will represent the region AB of the initial magnetization curve, below the 'knee' (Fig. 12.5). Crystal imperfections, particularly those of size comparable with the thickness of the domain wall, will impede the movement of the wall, and the wall will only be able to 'jump past' the obstacle when the field has built up sufficiently. In this way energy is dissipated in a way resembling the 'stick and slip' of mechanical friction. This irreversible process is responsible for the steeply rising part BC of the magnetization curve, and the energy dissipation is responsible for the hysteresis loop. Finally, at sufficiently high fields, the domains now present, which are still based on the easy direction in the material, will become completely aligned with the field by rotation. This corresponds to the upper part CD of the magnetization curve, the approach to saturation.

12.11 **Magnetic materials—theory and practice.** In this way, a theory of ferromagnetism can be established, resting on empirical foundations in the concepts of internal fields and domains, with the latter determining the hysteresis properties of the material. We shall now consider the bearing of this theory on the practical use of magnetic materials. The practical applications are of two main types. The first is concerned to exploit the intensification and concentration of magnetic flux in electrical machines, while the second is concerned with permanent magnets. The former is frequently used in applications where there is a cyclic traversal of the hysteresis loop, and a loss of energy associated with that. Materials for this type of application should obviously have a hysteresis loop of small area as well as high permeability and saturation, and are called *soft* magnetic materials.

On the other hand, to be useful for permanent magnet work, a material having a hysteresis loop with high remanence is required, and this is likely to be associated with a hysteresis loop of large area. Such materials are said to be *hard* magnetic materials.

Probably the ideal soft magnetic material is highly pure iron, since the absence of impurities removes the main obstacles to domain-wall movement. The main disadvantage of this material is economic—commercial iron is difficult and costly to purify to the required extent.

The impurities commonly present in commercial iron tend to form heterogeneous inclusions whose dimensions are close to the thickness of

M

the domain walls, so that they are able to exert the maximum hindrance to domain wall movement. The addition of silicon to the iron removes a lot of impurities as a silicaceous slag, and helps to disperse the rest atomically throughout the iron. The drawback of adding silicon is that the saturation magnetization of the iron is greatly decreased (on the other hand the resistivity is higher so the eddy current losses are reduced), but it is feasible to add up to 5% of silicon, and various alloys of specific compositions within this range are widely used, some of them having their magnetic properties improved by grain orientation treatments. Collectively, these materials form the staple soft magnetic material for motor, generator, and transformer laminations.

A variety of iron-nickel alloys are valuable soft magnetic materials. They suffer the combined disadvantages of high cost and reduced saturation magnetization by comparison with pure iron, but have specific properties which make them valuable for small transformer, choke and relay cores, and for magnetic shielding (Mumetal).

An interesting specialized application of a magnetic material exploits the anisotropy of magnetization alluded to in Section 12.9. Associated with magnetization in a given crystal direction there is often a change in dimension (magnetostriction) which can be made large by using nickel or an alloy of Ni 45%, Fe 55%, both of which show prominent anisotropy. Material of this kind is an excellent means of producing ultrasonic waves of low frequency.

In producing a good 'hard' magnetic material the problems are the contrary ones—we need a material loaded with impurities in the form that will provide the maximum impediment to domain wall motion. This is achieved in cobalt steels (up to 35% Co), but it is seen to better advantage in aluminium-nickel-cobalt alloy (Alnico) where on cooling the molten mixture of constituents, a variety of mutually immiscible phases separate out, providing the conditions sought. The performance of this material is enhanced (Alcomax) if it is allowed to solidify and cool in a magnetic field. A drawback of the material is its hardness; for economical production it must be cast into its final form.

12.12 The nature of the internal field.   After dealing with ferromagnetism at some length, we must return to the fundamental question, so far unanswered: what is the nature of the internal field? It must be emphasized that purely magnetic interaction between neighbouring atoms is altogether too small to explain the known facts of ferromagnetism, although as indicated previously the effects of this type of interaction can be seen in many paramagnetic materials at low temperatures.

The answer to this question is provided by the exchange interaction mentioned in Section 3.4. The effect of this interaction is to relate purely electrostatic forces to the spin direction of the electrons concerned. In the case of neighbouring atoms, we have, for the energy of interaction of electrons

$$E = E_{\text{classical}} - W_{ss}'$$

where $E_{\text{classical}}$ is a simple Coulomb term, and W_{ss}' is the *exchange energy*. Since W_{ss}' is concerned with the mutual repulsion of the charge clouds, it depends on the size of the electron orbits concerned, and the separation of the atoms in the crystals. The sign of W_{ss}' depends on the relative orientation of the electron spins concerned—we are taking W_{ss}' as being positive when the spins are parallel. The appropriate figures for the elements show that W_{ss}' is negligible for most materials, but rises to significant values for the transition metals. In the middle of the group W_{ss}' changes sign. It is positive for iron, cobalt and nickel (the ferromagnetic elements) and negative for the other transition elements. This means that for ferromagnetic materials the crystal energy will be a minimum if the spins are aligned parallel, and this will correspond to the undisturbed configuration of the crystal. We might conceive of this state of affairs being brought about by a magnetic force; calculation shows that such a force will be of such a magnitude as to agree with the experimental value of the Weiss field constant (Section 12.5). It is striking that the electron property responsible for ferromagnetism (the exchange energy) should also be a powerful element in determining the chemistry of the atom.

12.13 **Antiferromagnetism.** What of the other transition elements, in which the sign of W_{ss}' is reversed? Here the state of minimum energy requires neighbouring spins to be oppositely orientated, so that we cannot expect large susceptibilities. This phenomenon is known as *antiferromagnetism*. The ordering of the spins will break down at a temperature analogous to the Curie temperature, and called the *Néel point* (after the discoverer of the phenomenon). It will come as no surprise to learn that there are no practical applications of antiferromagnetism, and we shall not discuss it further.

12.14 **Ferrimagnetism.** A situation similar to antiferromagnetism— a lattice with neighbouring spins oppositely ordered—can be envisaged in a lattice containing two different magnetic ions. The opposed magnetic moments will now not be equal, and a finite magnetic polarization should be attainable. This phenomenon is described as *Ferrimagnetism*. To this category belongs lodestone, the first magnetic material to be discovered; an oxide of iron in which the two magnetic moments are both iron, but in different valence states, and with different spins.

A surprising feature in this material arises from the presence of oxygen, which in fact dilutes the magnetic ions to a separation far beyond the range of exchange interactions. The oxygen, however, is not a mere diluent, but acts as a carrier of exchange 'information' in a process called 'super-exchange'; we shall make no attempt to describe this process in detail (see Reference 1 at the end of the chapter). The oxygen is important for this reason: it prevents the occurrence of metallic conductivity while still permitting magnetic ordering. The oxide is in fact a semiconductor of such poor conductivity as to be virtually an insulator (this is a result of the low electron mobility characteristic of oxides). It is this property which makes ferrimagnetic materials interesting from the practical point of view —all known ferromagnetics are metals having the drawback that applications involving cyclic magnetization give rise to losses due to eddy currents. At low frequencies the use of laminations is sufficient to reduce the losses but in the radio-frequency range the use of ferromagnetic cores in transformers and inductances is impossible. The advent of a magnetic non-conductor removes this limitation; this is the advantage of ferrimagnetic materials.

12.15 **Ferrites.** Magnetic oxide of iron is not as it stands a very satisfactory material; there is however a large sequence of similar materials with the same crystal structure, produced by 'ringing the changes' on the magnetic ions present. These materials are called *ferrites*, and we shall consider a few important examples. It should be borne in mind here that ferrimagnetics share many of the properties of ferromagnetics including saturation (the saturation magnetization will necessarily be rather low because of the opposed spins), domain structure, and hysteresis.

In the ferrites of practical importance the divalent iron in magnetic iron oxide is replaced by one or more of the elements: Mn, Mg, Ni, Co, Cu, Zn, Cd, Ba. As in the case of ferromagnetic materials (Section 12.11), we can usefully distinguish soft ferrites; of these manganese-zinc and nickel-zinc ferrites (Ferroxcube A and B) are of particular importance for the cores of inductances and transformers at radio frequencies, for aerial rods, and similar applications.

As would be expected, the materials of importance as hard ferrites (notably barium ferrite, Ferroxdure) have a different crystal structure, and one which is subject to considerable distortion on magnetization. Ferrite permanent magnets find application in television receivers as focus units, ion trap magnets and picture-shape correctors.

Magnesium manganese ferrite is notable as having a square hysteresis loop; this makes it especially suitable for use in computer storage.

As already stated, the ferrites, by virtue of their low conductivity, are free from eddy current losses. Some are remarkable also for their freedom from losses associated with domain wall movement, and these can be used up to microwave frequencies. Here new properties become effective—the Larmor precession of the spins in a fixed magnetic field can be in resonance with the microwave field. If the latter is plane polarized, then at resonance the plane of polarization will be rotated; this property can be used to make a non-reciprocal network (ferrite isolator) in a waveguide system, for instance to exclude pump power from the detector of a maser (15·8).

REFERENCES

1. BLACKMAN, L. C. F. 'Cooperative magnetism in oxide structures', Pt. 1 and 2, *Research* **12**, 164 and 218 (1959).

2. LEE, E. W., *Magnetism*, Penguin Books, London (1963).

3. PARASNIS, D. S., *Magnetism*, Hutchinson, London (1961).

PROBLEMS

12.1   Regarding the electron as a charged sphere, and ignoring quantum effects, calculate
    (i) the magnetic moment of an electron in a circular orbit
    (ii) the magnetic moment of a spinning electron
in terms of the angular momentum in each case.

12.2   Calculate the potential energy of a magnetic dipole of moment μ, respectively parallel and antiparallel to an applied field B.
    Having regard to electron spin, a magnetic field will change the energy of electrons in a metal. The electrons will subsequently take up new states of minimum energy, and as a result the metal will have a paramagnetic susceptibility. Calculate this at $0°K$, for the free electron model.
    (Hint: Electrons with spins aligned with the field will have to reverse their orientation. Use the density of states function to find the number involved.)

12.3   The atomic number of iron is 26; following the scheme of Sections 2.12 and 2.13, write down the quantum numbers of each electron. What is the total angular momentum, orbital and spin, for the ion Fe^{++}?
    What is the magnetic susceptibility of a solution of $FeSO_4$ containing 1 gram mole/litre of $FeSO_4 \cdot 7H_2O$ at $300°K$? What is the saturation magnetisation of metallic iron, density $7·85. 10^3 kg/m^3$?

12.4   The $FeSO_4$ solution of the previous question is in a field of $0·2$ weber/m². What proportion of the atomic moments are parallel to the field?

12.5   A microwave cavity at $4 \cdot 2°$K contains a ruby crystal (aluminium oxide with a trace of Cr^{+++} impurity). It gives a resonance at 9220 Mc/s in a magnetic field of $0 \cdot 423$ weber/m². Calculate the g-value of Cr^{+++}. What magnetic field would be required to tune the resonance to 10,200 Mc/s?

12.6   In a specimen of n-type InSb at $2 \cdot 2°$K, a cyclotron resonance is obtained at 23,975 Mc/s, in a magnetic field of $0 \cdot 15$ weber/m². What is the effective mass of the electrons? What kind of electron mobility would you expect as a result?

Chapter 13

Dielectric Materials

13.1 Description of dielectric properties. The starting point of electrostatics is the force between charges *in vacuo*, but in dealing with experimental situations involving bulk matter it is scarcely possible to take account of every charged particle separately. Fortunately it is not necessary to do so. We can approach the problem empirically, and regard matter as either conducting, in which case it contains free charge whose properties we have already discussed, or dielectric. The most conspicuous property of a dielectric is that if a sheet of dielectric material be interposed between the plates of a condenser at potential V, the charge on the plates is decreased—in a ratio which defines the *dielectric constant* of the material. The decrease in the charge is interpreted as due to the appearance of charge of opposite sign at the surface of the dielectric. Charge in the dielectric is not free to move, but the effect could be produced if a large number of parallel dipoles were produced in the dielectric; the charge would cancel out everywhere but at the surfaces.

We can define a quantity **P**—the *polarization*—as the dipole moment per unit volume. It is usually proportional to the field
$$\mathbf{P} = \chi \varepsilon_0 \mathbf{F}_0;$$

χ is the electric susceptibility.

If we wish to apply Gauss' Theorem to a dielectric without taking explicit account of the polarization, we must work in terms of the electric displacement **D** where
$$\mathbf{D} = \varepsilon_0 \mathbf{F}_0 + \mathbf{P}.$$

Now defining dielectric constant ε as above,
$$\mathbf{D} = \varepsilon \varepsilon_0 \mathbf{F}_0$$
and
$$\mathbf{P} = (\varepsilon - 1)\, \varepsilon_0\, \mathbf{F}_0 \tag{1}$$

13.2 The limitations of the band theory for dielectrics. These are the fundamental qualities we need in order to discuss the properties of a dielectric. The problem of this chapter is to interpret these in terms of atomic properties. The approach made in Chapter 10 is not very helpful here. We can identify an insulating crystal with a semiconductor of wide band gap, but we should also expect that in general there would be sufficient impurities present to confer a considerable conductivity upon such a semiconductor. Thus silicon carbide is a wide gap semiconductor, but as prepared it always has a low resistance, whereas the same is not true of diamond, or of sulphur. The reasons for this difference are obscure, but in any case the materials with which we are now concerned are frequently not crystalline and are often composed of tangled chains each made of many smaller molecules bonded together, the so-called *polymers*. Examples are rubber, polythene, and indeed all synthetic plastics. Other important insulating materials are liquids, again without the long range order characteristic of a crystal. In dealing with these materials, we shall have to deal with the properties of the molecules themselves, since there are no regularities of structure on the larger scale which we can profitably study at present.

13.3 **Permanent molecular dipoles.**   In any molecule there will be centres of positive charge at the nuclei of the constituent atoms, and a distribution of negative charge associated with the electrons. We can distinguish at once two kinds of atoms; the first, of which examples are H_2 and CCl_4, are so symmetrical that the centres of the two charge distributions are identical. At distances from such a molecule which are large compared with its size, there will be no steady electric field. For the second kind, represented by H_2O (actually $\overset{H_{\searrow}}{\underset{H_{\nearrow}}{}}O$) and HCl, this is not true. The electron affinities of oxygen and chlorine are greater than that of hydrogen, so the electrons in the molecule tend to be concentrated rather closer to the former. Using the language of Section 3.7 the bonding is ionic rather than covalent, and since the 'centres of gravity' of the positive and negative charges do not coincide, there will be a permanent dipole moment associated with these molecules, which are said to be *polar*. Notice that, with regard to the molecule of water, if its molecular structure were H—O—H, it would not have a permanent dipole moment, so that the measurement of this quantity is of considerable value in establishing molecular structure.

13.4 **Induced molecular dipoles.**   The distinction we have drawn between polar and non-polar molecules refers to the *equilibrium* configuration of the molecule. In an electric field, conditions will be different, the distribution of charge will change, and there will arise in every case an *induced* dipole moment in the direction of the field, regardless of whether the molecule is polar or non-polar. The distortion produced by fields of physically realizable magnitude on the charge distribution is always small;

we may therefore express it as a power series in $\mathbf{F}$, neglecting all terms of order higher than the first. Thus we have

$$\mathbf{p} = a\,\mathbf{F} \tag{2}$$

where $\mathbf{p}$ is the induced dipole moment, $\mathbf{F}$ the field, and the coefficient a is the *polarizability* of the material. Now this gives, for $\mathbf{P}$,

$$\mathbf{P} = na\,\mathbf{F} \tag{3}$$

where n is the number of molecules per unit volume.

13.5   The Clausius-Misotti equation. It is more difficult to proceed further, because the field experienced by any individual molecule, which enters into the expressions (2) and (3), is not necessarily the same as the applied field $\mathbf{F_0}$ of equation (1) and we must find some way of relating the two. Our general problem of relating the macroscopic properties of dielectrics to the molecular properties now reduces to this more precise issue, for in fact any given molecule will experience not only the applied field, but the dipole fields of neighbouring molecules as well. An approximate value of the latter contribution was given by Lorentz for the case of a liquid or a gas, in which the molecules will be moving randomly. The approximation holds good also for a crystal provided it has cubic symmetry.

The Lorentz result is

$$\mathbf{F} = \mathbf{F_0} + \mathbf{P}/3\varepsilon_0,$$

which gives, since $\mathbf{P} = na\,\mathbf{F} = na\,[\mathbf{F_0} + \mathbf{P}/3\varepsilon_0]$, and $\mathbf{P} = (\varepsilon - 1)\,\varepsilon_0\mathbf{F_0}$:

$$\frac{\varepsilon - 1}{\varepsilon + 2} = \frac{na}{3\varepsilon_0},$$

the *Clausius-Misotti* equation.

For a non-polar gas $\varepsilon \simeq 1$, so we may write

$$\varepsilon - 1 = \frac{na}{\varepsilon_0},$$

which in fact is equivalent to putting $\mathbf{F} = \mathbf{F_0}$ and ignoring the effect of the gas itself on the local field. The validity of the full expression has been established for non-polar liquids. It is not possible in general to calculate the polarizability or to determine its value independently.

13.6   The behaviour of polar molecules.   For polar molecules the internal field will be somewhat different. It would be the same if the orientations of the permanent dipoles were random, but effectively a small proportion of them will be aligned by the field, against the disordering effect of thermal movement, as in the case of a paramagnetic material (Section 12.4). If allowance is made for this difference, we have an increase in a of $\mathbf{p}^2/3\mathbf{k}T$; the inclusion of this term gives reasonable agreement with experiment for the behaviour of polar gases, or for dilute solutions of polar molecules in non-polar solvents, but for polar liquids and solids it gives absurd results. The resemblance to the magnetic case would lead us to anticipate the saturation of the polarization, and spontaneous polarization; the Clausius-Misotti equation indeed predicts this, for instance for water below a 'Curie temperature' of 1000°K.

Now in fact spontaneous electric polarization ('ferroelectricity') is known, but it is a comparatively rare phenomenon, restricted to a small number of crystals of complex lattice structure. There are close parallels between ferroelectricity and ferromagnetism, including the existence of domain structure and the occurrence of hysteresis, but we will not discuss this further here. The essential point is that ferroelectricity is less common than theory would lead us to suppose, and it was pointed out by Onsager that the Lorentz expression for the internal field is inaccurate when this field is not small. When appropriate modifications are made we find that the possibility of ferroelectricity arising in this way is now eliminated, and that better agreement with the observed dielectric constants of polar liquids is attained.

13.7 **Dielectrics in alternating fields.** Up to this point, we have been considering the dielectric constant in a static field, but in practice it is the behaviour in alternating fields that is more important. To go to an extreme case, we can identify the dielectric constant at optical frequencies with the square of the refractive index, but there is often found to be a disagreement between radio-frequency and optical measurements, and the refractive indices at X-ray wavelengths have no resemblance at all to optical values. These discrepancies arise because in traversing such a wide range of frequencies, we cover many resonances of these electrons in the molecule. In calculating the instantaneous dipole moment and hence ε by the Clausius-Misotti equation, it is found that the value decreases as the frequency increases through a resonance. (Fig. 13.1). Possible resonances which will affect the dielectric constant are:

(i) Electronic transitions within the atoms of a molecule. These will give changes in ε in the ultra-violet and X-ray region, and are responsible for the anomalous X-ray refractive index just mentioned.

(ii) Molecular vibration frequencies, in the short wavelength infra-red region.

(iii) Rotation bands, in the far infra-red and microwave region. This will only affect the dielectric constant if the molecule is polar, since only then can a rotating molecule interact with an alternating field.

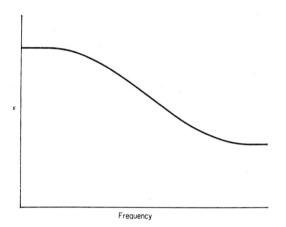

Frequency

FIG. 13.1 Decrease in dielectric constant as the frequency is swept through a resonance. For a given material, the graph over a wider range of frequencies may include several 'steps' of this kind.

The last of these factors is responsible for the large dielectric constant of water at low frequencies—it is due to the contribution of the permanent dipoles. Above a certain frequency, the reorientation of the dipoles will be unable to keep pace with the field. In solids molecular rotation is often prevented altogether—as witness the dielectric constant of ice, which is small compared with that of liquid water. The limitation is due to geo-metrical factors, for if molecules are packed in a crystal lattice, there is unlikely to be room for them to rotate. There is a marked contrast here with the magnetic properties, when the spins can readily orient themselves to the applied field in the crystal—but the quenching of orbital contribu-tions to the magnetic moment is a comparable effect.

PROBLEMS

13.1 The following table gives data on the polarization of two related molecules, carbon tetrachloride CCl_4 and methyl chloride CH_3Cl, at different temperatures. What are the dipole moments of each?

$T°K$	CCl_4	CH_3Cl
	P	P
1000	9.3×10^{-5}	11.3×10^{-5}
500	9.3×10^{-5}	20.7×10^{-5}
330	9.3×10^{-5}	30.0×10^{-5}
250	9.3×10^{-5}	39.3×10^{-5}

13.2 From the table in Question 13.1, calculate the radius a of each molecule, regarding it as a conducting sphere of polarization $4\pi\varepsilon_0 a^3$.

13.3 Prove the expression quoted in Section 8.15 for the dielectric constant of an ionized gas.
(Hint: Consider the conduction and displacement currents produced by a sinusoidal field, and regard their combined effect as a displacement current with an 'effective' dielectric constant.)
Why do we not consider the motion of positive ions?
A radio wave of frequency 1·25 Mc/s is reflected from a height of 100 km. What is the electron density at this height?

Chapter 14

Electrical Noise

14.1 Is indefinite amplification possible? At a first glance, it might appear that there is no lower limit to the magnitude of electric current we can hope to measure. One can imagine the sensitivity of a moving coil galvanometer to be increased indefinitely by reduction of the torsion constant of the suspension, and by increasing the length of the optical lever arm. Alternatively, by successive stages of carefully designed valve amplifiers, it should be possible to amplify a current, no matter how small, to an arbitrarily large extent. In physics certainly it is often necessary to be able to measure very small effects of all kinds, but the problem is less academic than that; in communications, and in radar, the detection of marginal signals assumes an obvious importance.

14.2 Physical limitations of amplification—noise. We encounter at once a difficulty of principle. A sensitive radio receiver operating at full gain gives a characteristic hissing sound in the loudspeaker even when no transmitted signal reaches the aerial, and the displayed sweep of a sensitive radar is not a uniform horizontal line in the absence of a definite echo, but is thickened and undulating on account of random vertical deflections. From the first of these examples, the phenomenon is described as electrical *noise*, and in either example it is clear that in competition with it, a weak signal will be unintelligible. Further amplification is of no avail, since it operates on the noise as well as the signal and only transcribes the problem unchanged in its essentials to a range of higher amplitudes. Before we can see how to improve the situation, we must discuss the nature of the noise, and this we shall do in the present chapter.

We can distinguish between noise produced in the environment, and noise due to our equipment. The environmental noise is partly man-made —from car ignition systems and similar disturbances. There is also a residue of 'natural' noise, both radiation produced outside the earth and its atmosphere, and the 'atmospherics' due to those thunderstorms which are a permanent occurrence at one place or another on the earth's surface. The latter are primarily a low frequency phenomenon and provide an ultimate limitation to the use of long radio wavelengths for communications,

one about which nothing can be done. At higher frequencies, radio noise
of cosmic origin predominates. At still higher frequencies, in the ultrahigh
frequency and microwave regions, this kind of disturbance is again of little
importance, and the limiting factors are due to our detecting apparatus.
Here at least we can hope to improve matters, and the kind of noise that
arises under these conditions is naturally more interesting; we shall devote
the remainder of the chapter to its examination.

14.3 **An example—the reflecting galvanometer.** Let us turn
away from electronics for a moment, and consider the example with which
we began: that of a reflecting galvanometer of great sensitivity. This simple
device is not free from the bane of noise, which here takes the form of
random fluctuations of the coil on either side of the zero position, even
when no signal is applied. These fluctuations appear regardless of whether
the galvanometer coil is open- or shortcircuited, though the form of the
fluctuations differs somewhat in the two cases.

The coil of the galvanometer is inevitably in thermal equilibrium with
its environment. Normally it is in contact with air at room temperature,
but even if it were suspended in high vacuum it would still be connected
with the world by way of the torsion suspension and the leads to the coil.
Being in equilibrium with the environment is shares the energy of the
environment. What share of this energy belongs to the suspended coil, and
in what form is it present?

The first of these questions and part of the second are answered,
characteristically in terms of great generality, by a thermodynamical
principle—the principle of equipartition of energy—which states that a
system in thermal equilibrium with its surroundings will have an *average*
energy of $\frac{1}{2}kT$ for each degree of freedom. The number of degrees of
freedom available is given by the number of squared terms necessary to
specify the kinetic energy exactly. In the case of a suspended coil there is
only one degree of freedom—it can simply rotate about its axis of suspension.

Suppose for the moment that the coil possesses energy of $\frac{1}{2}kT$ exactly;
this will be shared between potential and kinetic energy. If the stored
energy were all potential, then the coil would necessarily be at rest and
deflected from its zero position, since the only repository for potential
energy offered by the system is the elastic energy in the deflected suspension. This would lead to a deflection θ given by

$$\tfrac{1}{2}c\theta^2 = \tfrac{1}{2}kT$$

where c is the tension constant of the suspension

Now a deflection is as likely in one direction as another, and in any case part of the energy of the suspension may be kinetic, which implies motion; thus we have a picture of a randomly fluctuating coil whose kinetic energy is zero at those instants when a maximum of the deflection has been reached (correspondingly, as the suspension passes through its zero, its energy is, entirely kinetic). Remembering that equipartition of energy is only an average result, we can apply the above not to any specific fluctuation, but to the average of all so that we have

$$\overline{\theta^2} = kT/c,$$

where $\overline{\theta^2}$ is the mean square value of the amplitudes of all fluctuations.

Notice the generality of this result. It is not *necessarily* true that the fluctuations are due to the bombardment of the coil by air molecules, and arise because in a small interval of time the number of such bombardments on opposite sides will be unequal. This *may* be a mechanism, but we do not get rid of the fluctuations by pumping out the air surrounding the suspension; we do not even change their average amplitude, though we may alter their rate.

Again, if we have small particles (but large enough to be seen under the microscope) in suspension in a liquid, they will be in equilibrium with the molecules of the liquid, and will participate in the random kinetic energy of the molecules on equal terms. What we shall see is the random motion of the particle representing this kinetic energy—the well-known *Brownian motion* which is a more familiar example than the galvanometer suspension, though it illustrates exactly the same principles.

14.4 **Application to a tuned circuit.** We can extend these arguments to a case which is more directly related to our interests—a tuned circuit, with inductance, capacitance and resistance in series. By analogy, the energy in the inductance is equivalent to kinetic energy in the galvanometer example, the energy in the condenser to potential energy. We can therefore write

$$\tfrac{1}{2}c\overline{V^2} = \tfrac{1}{2}L\overline{\dot{i}^2} = \tfrac{1}{2}kT,$$

where $\overline{V^2}$ is the mean square value of the potential difference across the condenser plates.

We can rewrite this in terms of a fluctuating e.m.f. e with the resistance as load:

$$\overline{e^2} = kT/C.$$

14.5 **Frequency spectrum of the fluctuations.** This takes us to the same point we reached in discussing the galvanometer suspension, but in a typical case $\sqrt{(\overline{e^2})}$ is of the order of microvolts, and a high gain amplifier will be necessary if the fluctuations are to be detected. The bandwidth of a suitable amplifier will not be large, and we therefore require to know something of the frequency spectrum of the fluctuating e.m.f.—to find out what the r.m.s. voltage in a bandwidth Δf centred on a frequency f will be. To do this we will approach the problem from a different viewpoint. If the fluctuation is regarded as due to rapidly moving electrons, then each will correspond to a current pulse charging C whose Fourier analysis will be a uniform frequency spectrum up to frequencies of the order of the reciprocal of the duration of the impulse—which takes us to very high frequencies indeed. Therefore, the contribution of any one of the impulses in a bandwidth Δf is proportional to Δf, and since separate impulses occur at random phases, we may add their contributions to get

$$\overline{e_f^2} = \text{const } \Delta f = E\Delta f.$$

Now the fluctuating e.m.f. e_f produces a voltage v_f across the condenser:

$$v_f = \frac{e_f}{LC\omega^2 - 1 + jRC\omega},$$

and its average value is

$$\frac{\overline{e_f^2}}{(\omega^2 LC - 1)^2 + R^2 C^2 \omega^2} = \frac{1}{2\pi} \frac{E\, d\omega}{(\omega^2 LC - 1)^2 + R^2 C^2 \omega^2}.$$

This is the required expression, but it includes the unknown E; to eliminate it integrate over all frequencies to get the total fluctuation

$$\overline{v^2} = \frac{E}{4RC}.$$

By comparison with the equation we had earlier ($\overline{v^2} = kT/C$),

$$E = 4kTR$$

or

$$\overline{e_f^2} = 4kTR\, \Delta f.$$

Substituting back, we have

$$\overline{v_f^2} = \frac{4kTR\Delta f}{(1 - \omega^2 LC)^2 + R^2 C^2 \omega^2}.$$

14.6 **Johnson noise.** Notice that the r.m.s. noise voltage does not depend on R, but that the frequency dependence does. In particular, if R is small, the noise is concentrated in those frequencies near the resonance for the given values of L and C in the circuit. In practice we are most interested in the noise generated in a single resistor. In such a case L is negligible and $R^2\omega^2 C^2$ will only be appreciable at very high frequencies. Otherwise, the fluctuating voltage across its terminals will be identical with e_f.

We could equally well have worked in terms of a fluctuating current i_t rather than e_t—it is a matter of taste whether we think of an 'ideal' noiseless resistance in series with a random voltage generator or in parallel with a random current generator. What is of more fundamental importance is the noise *power*. We are likely to be interested in the noise in the grid resistor of the first stage of an amplifier. The maximum power that can be transferred to the valve will be given when the matching condition is satisfied and will be

$$W = kT\Delta f.$$

At room temperature

$$W = 4 \times 10^{-21} \, \Delta f \text{ watts.}$$

This type of noise is often referred to as *Johnson noise*. It is 'white' noise (i.e. with a flat frequency spectrum) and its r.m.s. value does not depend on the magnitude of the resistor. Johnson noise will be observed when the resistor is carrying no steady current. If a steady current is flowing there will sometimes be additional noise, *current noise* with an entirely different spectrum, for the noise per unit bandwidth is found to increase as the reciprocal of the frequency. Noise of this sort seems to be characteristic of metallic films and semiconductors (including carbon resistors).

14.7 **Physical nature of Johnson noise.**   Johnson noise represents the ultimate limitation on the performance of electronic equipment, and no discussion of electrical noise could omit it. Yet there is a sense in which it is out of place in this book. The book discusses in the main those matters of engineering which follow directly from the physical properties of the electron. Now we have discussed Johnson noise in terms of electronic fluctuations, but only to tie down our discussion to something tangible. Like the fluctuations in the galvanometer coil, the theoretical basis of the analysis is thermodynamic, which gives to the conclusions a generality which reaches beyond any particular model. *Johnson noise would still be observed if electricity were a homogeneous fluid.* The significant feature is this: neither the electronic charge nor any other property of the electron appears in the expression for the Johnson noise which we have here derived.

There are fluctuation phenomena which do arise from the discrete nature of the electron. Not surprisingly these will appear in their simplest form when we consider a current made up simply of a stream of electrons, that is, a vacuum diode. We shall now discuss this kind of noise.

14.8 **Shot noise.**   Imagine a diode where the current is temperature-limited, i.e. operating on the saturation part of its characteristic. We

N

choose this region because the emission of each electron from the cathode is a random event, and each electron makes its way to the anode independently of any other.

Consider first the transit of one electron from cathode to anode. The current i flowing in the anode circuit as the electron crosses the cathode-anode space will represent the flow of induced charge from one electrode to the other. All we know about the shape of the resulting current pulse is that its length is given by τ the transit time of the electron, and the area under it, $q = \int_{-\tau/2}^{+\tau/2} i\, dt$, is the electronic charge. Like any other mathematical function, we can express it as a Fourier series

$$i = a_0 + \sum_{n=1}^{\infty} a_n \cos \frac{2\pi nt}{T} + \sum_{n=1}^{\infty} b_n \sin \frac{2\pi nt}{T},$$

where T is an arbitrary time interval, which we associate with the time over which we sample the current.

We can determine a_0, a_n, b_n from the standard expressions for Fourier coefficients:

$$a_0 = \frac{1}{T} \int_{-T/2}^{+T/2} i\, dt, \quad a_n = \frac{2}{T} \int_{-T/2}^{+T/2} i \cos \left(\frac{2\pi nt}{T}\right) dt,$$

$$b_n = \frac{2}{T} \int_{-T/2}^{+T/2} i \sin \left(\frac{2\pi nt}{T}\right) dt.$$

The integrals can be evaluated provided that we limit ourselves to frequencies smaller than the reciprocal of the transit time. The current is only finite over τ, and for this time period

$$\sin (2\pi nt/T) = 0, \text{ and } \cos (2\pi nt/T) = 1.$$

This supposes that T is large compared with the transit time. Under these conditions the Fourier components will appear not as a series of harmonics but as continuous frequency distribution and we have

$$2a_0 = a_n = \frac{2}{T} \int_{-T/2}^{+T/2} i\, dt = \frac{2e}{T},$$

and therefore

$$i = \frac{e}{T} + \sum_{n=1}^{\infty} \frac{2e}{T} \cos \left(\frac{2\pi nt}{T} \right),$$

and this gives the mean square value of the nth Fourier component,

$$\overline{i^2}_n = \frac{2e^2}{T^2}.$$

So far we have considered a single electron. If N electrons arrive in the time T, they will make similar contributions, but of random phases. Therefore, we add the intensities, and have again for the nth Fourier component

$$\overline{i_n^2} = \frac{2e^2 N}{T^2},$$

or, in terms of the total current I,

$$\overline{i_n{}^2} = \frac{2eI}{T}.$$

Now, our measurements will be confined to a bandwidth Δf which will contain $T\Delta f$ of these Fourier components, so we can write, for the r.m.s. fluctuation observed,

$$\Delta \overline{i_n{}^2} = 2eI\Delta f.$$

This expression gives the *shot noise* of the diode, representing the fluctuation in current arising because the smallest unit of charge in transit is finite, and the number arriving in successive intervals fluctuates. Notice that, as indicated at the beginning of this section, the expression depends on the value of the electronic charge; it would be zero for conduction by a continuous fluid.

14.9 **Noise reduction by space charge.** This result does *not* apply to a space-charge limited diode because, in the nature of things, in a space charge one electron is certainly not independent of the others. The correlation reduces the shot noise in a diode by a factor of up to 100.

14.10 **Partition noise.** In a diode all the current leaving the cathode must reach the anode, but this will not necessarily be true in a tetrode or pentode, where the current divides itself between anode and screen. The proportion of the current reaching the anode is a random quantity and this gives rise to *partition noise*. For a tetrode, it has been shown that

$$\overline{i_f} = 2eI \left(\frac{i_g + \Gamma^2 i_a}{i_g + i_a} \right) \Delta f,$$

where i_g is the current to the screen grid, i_a that to the anode, and Γ is the space charge smoothing factor mentioned in the previous paragraph. Note that if $\Gamma = 1$ the partition noise expression reduces to the shot noise. Shot noise is already quite random, and its fluctuating subdivision between two electrodes can make no difference since there are no degrees of randomness. The expression would apply for a triode when i_g is finite (grid positive) but there is no partition noise otherwise.

14.11 Flicker noise. Thermionic emission is responsible for another type of noise—*flicker noise*, which seems to be due to fluctuations in the work function of the cathode surface. Like current noise in semiconductors (Section 14.6), this increases in importance at low frequencies. The noise increases with the current through the valve. In the audio-frequency range it is likely to exceed shot noise, but it may be minimized by the individual selection of a 'quiet' valve.

14.12 Noise in transistors. As would be expected, transistors whose action depends on the essentially random process of diffusion show noise comparable with shot and partition noise. The reader is referred to more advanced books for details.

14.13 Equivalent temperature or noise factor. Considerations of noise are often of importance in the design of equipment, especially radio receivers. The noise level in a receiver can often be reduced by deliberately mismatching the aerial and the grid resistor of the first stage, but the details are outside our scope. Even when all precautions are taken, it will inevitably happen that the noise output of a receiver will be higher than the theoretical minimum of $kT\,\Delta f$. The ratio of the actual to the ideal noise level for a receiver is known as the *noise figure* or *noise factor*. In view of the nature of the expression for the noise of the ideal receiver it is sometimes illuminating to express noise factor in terms of *equivalent temperature*.

REFERENCES

1. BELL, D. A., *Electrical Noise*, Van Nostrand, London (1960).

2. MACDONALD, D. K. C. *Noise and Fluctuations*, Wiley, New York (1962).

PROBLEMS

14.1 An amplifier has a uniform gain G over a frequency interval Δf centred upon f. A resistance R is placed across the input, and the output power measured. How is this related to the fluctuations of current in the resistor? The input to the amplifier is found to be doubled if the resistor is in series with a saturated diode passing a mean current I. Show how a value of the electronic charge can be deduced from these measurements. Express the 'effective' bandwidth Δf above more realistically in terms of a gain $G(f)$ which varies with frequency.

14.2 A triode has a g_m of 5 mA/V. A resistance is connected between cathode and grid, and cooled until the noise arising from it is equal to the shot noise of the valve. This condition is satisfied at 200°K, when the value of its resistance is 300 Ω. If the anode current of the triode is 10 mA, what is the space charge smoothing factor?

Chapter 15

Molecular Amplification

15.1 Practical limitations imposed by noise. In Chapter 14 the problem of noise in electric circuits was considered. A particular application of this concerns the detection of weak radio signals at microwave frequencies. In this region of the electromagnetic spectrum, one's ultimate limitation is cosmic noise, generated deep in space. The noise level at these wavelengths is very low, however, and if a receiver is to be made to take full advantage of this situation, it must have a very low noise figure indeed. Now a mixer stage is inevitably noisy, so one would normally precede it with some amplification at signal frequency. How is that to be done? A travelling-wave tube (Section 6.16) could be used to amplify the signal, but it is a very noisy device, owing to the shot noise in the cathode which supplies the beam. Expressing the noise figure of the amplifier in terms of equivalent temperature (Section 14.13), a typical value would be $1200°K$. The noise temperature of space near the zenith at a wavelength of 3 cm is only about $3°K$, so the travelling-wave tube is woefully inadequate. For sensitive radar installations, for satellite communications, and for the exploration of space to look for discrete sources of radiation (radio astronomy) something much better is needed.

15.2 A new approach—molecular amplification. The solution of these difficulties that we are about to discuss involves the abandonment of macroscopic active circuit elements in favour of atomic ones. It is hardly surprising, in view of the revolutionary nature of the change, that our whole approach to the problem must be transformed; for instance quantum theory will be found to govern the behaviour of a 'molecular amplifier'. The transformation of our thought of which this is part is one of the most exciting developments in electron physics, and it is fitting that an account of it should conclude this book.

15.3 Lifetime of excited electronic states. It will be best if we forget for the moment our ulterior motive of looking for a low noise amplifier, and consider for its own sake, and rather more closely than we have done so far, the problem of the emission and absorption of photons by atoms.

In Chapter 2 we have interpreted the permitted energies of an atom in terms of single electron states. Consider one such electron in the ground state E_1. It can be excited to a state E_2 by the absorption of a photon of frequency ν_{21} given by

$$h\nu_{21} = E_2 - E_1.$$

At a subsequent time, the atom will return to its ground state with the re-emission of a photon of energy $h\nu_{21}$. How long does the electron spend in the excited state before re-emission? The problem can be regarded first of all as similar to that of the disintegration of a radioactive nucleus,— that is to say, as a completely random process. Hence in a population of excited atoms the number returning to the ground state at a given instant is proportional to the number of excited atoms at that instant, i.e.

$$\frac{dn}{dt} \propto n$$

or
$$n = n_0 \exp(t/\tau),$$

where the constant τ defines the 'lifetime' of the excited state just as we may define the lifetime of a radioactive nucleus. The lifetimes of atomic excited states are usually of the order 10^{-8} sec but if the optical transition to the ground state is 'forbidden', which usually means that the excited state was reached by an indirect route, the lifetime will be longer, 10^{-4} sec or more. These are the 'metastables' of Section 7.10.

15.4 **Spontaneous and stimulated emission.** Equipped with this picture of the absorption and emission of radiation by the atom, we can consider the atom in thermal equilibrium in a closed box. The radiation inside the box will be 'black body' radiation—in other words, the number of photons of given energy will be uniquely determined by the temperature. In addition temperature will fix the proportion of atoms in the excited state, which will be given by the Boltzmann distribution

$$\frac{N(E_1)}{N(E_2)} = \exp \frac{-(E_2 - E_1)}{kT},$$

where $N(E_1)$ and $N(E_2)$ are the populations of the states E_1, E_2 respectively. These two assertions governing the number of excited atoms and the number of photons respectively are both fundamental thermodynamic principles and should fit together into a consistent picture. Einstein drew attention to the fact that they do not—it appears that more energy is absorbed than emitted. To bring about the energy balance necessary for equilibrium, Einstein suggested that an extra term be introduced, corresponding to a second process of radiation emission. The second term is quite different from the first in that it represents a process whose *rate* (or probability) is *proportional to the intensity of radiation of frequency ν falling on the atom*. The radiation field stimulates the excited atom to emit, and we can constrast this process of *stimulated emission* with the more familiar process of *spontaneous* (random) emission. The latter is more familiar because it is overwhelmingly dominant so long as $h\nu/kT$ is large, and this is so in the optical and infra-red regions of the spectrum, where most of our accumulated experience lies. On the other hand, if $h\nu/kT$ is small (as it is in the microwave region), stimulated emission is the more important; as we shall see later however, stimulated emission in the visible region is conspicuous enough, once one has learnt how to look for it.

15.5 **Stimulated emission as photon amplification.** In terms of photons, stimulated emission appears as the interaction of the photon with an excited atom which leads to the emission by the atom of a second photon, identical with the primary. In other words *the photon has multiplied*. If we can find an atomic transition corresponding to a microwave frequency we could usefully think of applying this principle—of microwave amplification by the stimulated emission of radiation. The name 'maser' follows the modern usage of forming a new word from initial letters.

15.6 **Condition for amplification—population inversion.** To accomplish amplification it is only necessary to produce just more photons by stimulated emission than are lost by absorption. The details of the balance at equilibrium show that the *probability* of an atom in the ground state absorbing a photon, and of one in the excited state emitting one by stimulation, are equal; hence if amplification is to be possible, the *number* of atoms in the excited state must be greater than the number in the ground state. A look at the Boltzmann equation shows that this cannot be attained at any (positive) value of temperature, which means that it cannot be attained in thermal equilibrium. Our problem then is essentially one of disturbing equilibrium so as to bring about the *population inversion* required. We shall consider two ways in which this can be done.

15.7 **The ammonia maser.** The first depends on the process (quite literally) of picking out the excited atoms from the unexcited ones, and segregating them. This implausible procedure is in certain cases possible, the most notable involving the ammonia molecule, NH_3. The structure of this molecule is pyramidal, with the nitrogen atom at the vertex and the three hydrogen atoms forming the base. It is possible for the molecule to execute vibrations, in which the nitrogen atom vibrates back and forth through the plane of the hydrogen atoms, and the energy difference between this excited state and the ground state (no vibration) corresponds to a wavelength in the microwave region, about 3 cm in fact.

Because of its lack of symmetry, the molecule in the ground state will have a dipole moment (Section 13.3), but the average dipole moment of the molecule executing the vibrations we have described is zero. Now, if ammonia molecules are formed into a beam by allowing the gas to stream out of a collimating tube into a vacuum, and this beam is passed through a non-uniform electric field, the separation can be effected. The ground state molecules will be deflected by the non-uniform electric field, and lost to the beam; the excited molecules however, by virtue of their zero dipole moment, experience no deflecting force, and are introduced into a cavity resonant at the appropriate frequency. The cavity will then contain a preponderance of excited molecules, provided the lifetime of the excited state is long enough (as it will be at microwave frequencies).

If now an input signal of the resonant frequency is fed into the cavity, it can bring about spontaneous emission, and amplification will occur. The drawback of this arrangement is that the ammonia resonance cannot be tuned, and it represents an impracticably narrow bandwidth. On the other hand, like any other amplifier, it can be made to oscillate, and its former drawbacks now become virtues, so that it can be used as a very stable frequency standard—the 'ammonia clock'.

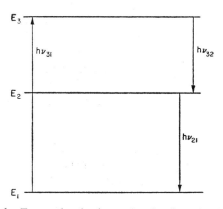

FIG. 15.1 Energy level scheme for the three level maser.

15.8 **The three level maser.** A much more versatile arrangement for achieving inversion is the *three level maser*. As the name implies, we here require not two but three energy levels associated with the same atomic or molecular system, with a similar separation (Fig. 15.1). A strong microwave signal of frequency ν_{31} corresponding to $E_3 - E_1$ raises some of the atoms to E_3; a limit is reached when the populations of E_3 and E_1 are the same, since then the radiation absorbed is just balanced by stimulated emission, a state of affairs known as 'saturation'. Now, not all the atoms in state E_3 will return directly to E_1 — some will return *via* E_2. By the choice of states of suitable lifetimes ($\tau_2 > \tau_3$) it is possible to arrange that the number of atoms in E_2 exceeds that in E_1 because the 'pump' frequency maintains a 'head' of atoms in E_3. Thus E_2 and E_1 are inverted and amplification is possible.

Suitable levels are found in a system very different from the ammonia molecule. The levels in question belong to the chromium ion; this can conveniently be used when it is present in small concentrations as an impurity in alumina crystals, a combination better known as the gemstone ruby. The advantage of these levels is that they are associated with electron states possessing a magnetic moment, so that the energy difference between them is not an inherent property of the ion, but depends on the presence of an external magnetic field (Section 12.3). The levels can therefore be tuned by variation of the magnetic field strength. In the absence of a pump signal, it is necessary that most of the ions should occupy the ground state, and this can be achieved only if the temperature of the ruby is lowered. Liquid helium temperatures are usually employed; this temperature (4°K) gives us the order of the equivalent noise temperature of the maser— about 10°K, and therefore an immense improvement over the travelling-wave tube. The ruby crystal is placed in a resonant cavity tuned both to the signal and to the pump frequency. The energy levels of the ions are somewhat broadened by the influence of the crystal, and so a useful bandwidth for amplification can be obtained. There are two drawbacks. One is the complexity associated with the operation of wavelengths and cavities at a very low temperature in a substantial magnetic field; the other is the need to provide a very strong pump signal at a higher frequency than the working frequency. It is, worth pointing out that the process giving rise to noise in the maser is spontaneous emission.

15.9   Coherence of molecular amplification.

One feature of molecular amplification of the greatest importance, which the simple treatment given in terms of photons does not bring out, is that the output has a fixed phase relationship to the input, in other words it is *coherent*. This is taken for granted in electronic circuits, but is unfamiliar in optics, where all our previous experience with atomic and molecular systems lies. This is because in optics we are normally dealing with spontaneous emission where the phase of the output is necessarily random with respect to the input.

15.10   Extension to optical frequencies—the laser.

There is nothing in the principle of the maser to limit its application to microwaves, and to prevent its application in the visible and infra-red regions. In recent years working devices, which are in fact oscillators and not amplifiers, have been made in this region of the spectrum; they are named *lasers* for obvious reasons (the name *iraser* also has currency). At these frequencies

$h\nu/kT \ll 1$, so the amount of stimulated emission to be expected is small. However, on account of its coherence, the cumulative intensity of stimulated emission is much greater than that from the same number of sources in random phase relationship, and this enhances the effect of the small number.

15.11 **The ruby laser.** The chromium ion in ruby again provides us with a suitable set of three levels, of which the highest is broadened by crystal interactions so that pumping can be conveniently achieved by the use of a high intensity photographic flash tube. The working frequency corresponds to red light. It is necessary that the interaction between the radiation and the ions should be as great as possible; this is best achieved by polishing plane parallel faces on opposite sides of the ruby and silvering them, so that repeated reflections of the light occur (in the case of the maser the resonant cavity serves the same purpose). The disadvantages of this arrangement are that very large amounts of pumping power are required, and that only pulsed emission is possible.

15.12 **The gas laser.** Continuous operation is possible in a gas system, where pump power can be provided by a discharge. Thus in helium, many atoms in a metastable state are produced in this way. The neon atom has an excited state very close in energy to the metastable helium, and energy transfer is possible on collision, by resonant transfer. Owing to the long lifetime of the helium metastable, this process is quite efficient, and inversion of the neon population can be achieved, not with respect to the ground state, but with respect to a lower excited state. The working wavelength is in the infra-red. To improve the interaction, the gas is confined between carefully aligned plane parallel, half-silvered plates.

15.13 **The semiconductor junction laser.** Recently a simple device has been developed, in which the inversion is caused by minority carrier injection in a semiconductor. This is done by applying a forward pulse of high current to a gallium arsenide p-n junction (Chapter 11), fabricated in a carefully cut and polished crystal (for repeated reflection of the light) and held at liquid nitrogen temperature ($90°K$). The operating wavelength is in the infra-red, corresponding approximately to the band gap energy ($1\cdot5$ eV) in the material.

15.14 **Applications of the laser.** The laser is of particular interest because it represents the first available source of coherent light. The potentialities of coherent light beams are considerable. Application to the communication field gives a huge bandwidth and information-carrying capacity hitherto undreamed of. On a very different plane, it is possible to focus a coherent beam to very small spot sizes where the incident flux represents an energy density of 10^6 watts/cm² (comparable with the maximum power density in an arc)—a concentration of power which has many possible applications in the field of high temperature technology. To range more widely, the physics of coherent light beams will lead inevitably to new developments in the science of optics, which will provide new fields for practical applications. The pattern of interaction between theory and practice, of which we have examined so many examples, will be extended to a completely new area in the science of electronics.

REFERENCES

1. LENGYEL, B. A. *Lasers*, Wiley, New York (1962).

2. SINGER, J. R. *Masers*, Wiley, New York (1959).

Periodic Table of the Elements

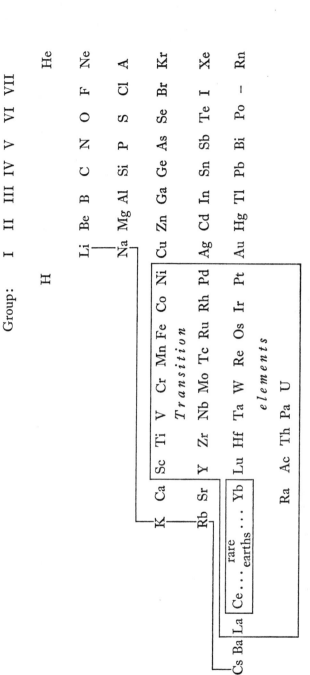

The atomic number (number of orbital electrons) increases from left to right across each row, and from top to bottom of the table, by integral steps.

General Bibliography

The books listed here have substantially the same scope as this book, or cover at least a majority of the topics we have discussed. Books of more specific interest are listed at the end of the appropriate chapter.

1. DEKKER, A. J. *Electrical Engineering Materials*, Prentice Hall, New York (1961).

2. DOW, W. G. *Fundamentals of Engineering Electronics*, 2nd edn., Wiley, New York (1952).

3. HEMENWAY, C. L., HENRY, R. W. and CAULTON, M. *Physical Electronics*, Wiley, New York (1962).

4. HUTCHINSON, T. S., and BAIRD, D. C. *The Physics of Engineering Solids*, Wiley, New York (1963).

5. RAMEY, R. L. *Physical Electronics*, Prentice Hall, London (1961).

6. RIDENOUR, L. N. (Ed.) *Modern Physics for the Engineer*, Series 1 and 2, McGraw-Hill, New York (1954, 1961).

7. THOMSON, J. and CALLICK, E. B. *Electron Physics and Technology*, English Universities Press, London (1959).

8. VAN DER ZIEL, A. *Solid State Physical Electronics*, Macmillan, London (1958).

9. VON HIPPEL, A. R. *et al. Molecular Science and Molecular Engineering*, Wiley and Technology Press, M.I.T., New York (1959).

Notes and Solutions to Problems

2.1 (a) 1·17 MeV, (b) 2·27 eV, (c) 4·13 × 10⁻⁵ eV; 5·33 × 10¹⁰, 2·7 × 10¹⁶, 1·5 × 10²¹. (The number of gamma quanta emitted corresponds to a radioactive source of strength 1·7 curies.)

2.3 10⁻³ m/sec; 10⁵ m/sec; 10¹⁰ m/sec. The corresponding uncertainties in energy are 10⁻¹⁸, 10⁻² and 3·10⁸ eV. The third of these figures represents an energy greater than the whole binding energy of the nucleus, and provides an argument that the nucleus cannot contain electrons (the volume in question is of the order of the nuclear volume).

2.4 3·88 × 10⁻¹⁰ m; 3·88 × 10⁻¹¹ m; 1·81 × 10⁻¹⁰ m; 2·86 × 10⁻¹⁴ m; 2·01 × 10⁻³⁸ m. The first and third are comparable with the interatomic spacing of crystals; the fourth is comparable with the diameter of the nucleus, and can produce nuclear reactions, and the last is so small compared with the dimensions of the body that no appreciable wave properties are displayed.

2.5 This is Bohr's treatment of the hydrogen atom; though mathematically naive, it has the merit of providing the familiar 'planetary' model of electron motion.

2.6 The lines represent the Balmer Series in the hydrogen spectrum. It was a comparison with this empirical result which indicated the value of Bohr's theory.
   (i) 1·6 × 10⁻¹⁹ coulomb
   (ii) 13·58 volts
   (iii) 5·3 × 10⁻¹¹ m
   (iv) 1640·49, 1215·18, 1084·98, 921·39.

3.1 4·43 eV; 1·27 Å. The first term in the expression represents the Coulomb attraction between two charged ions, the second a repulsive force arising from their electron charge clouds when they begin to overlap.

3.2 3·53 × 10¹⁷; 3·54 × 10¹³; 5·18 × 10¹⁹/m³.

3.3 1340 m/sec; 336 m/sec; $\frac{5}{2}$ kT and $\frac{3}{2}$ kT. Calculation suggests that the velocity of a proportion of any hydrogen in the high atmosphere would exceed the gravitational escape velocity, so that over a period this gas would be lost, while oxygen, etc., are retained.

3.4 10⁻³ mm.

3.6 3·53 × 10⁻¹⁰ m.

O

3.7   1·537.

4.1   4966 Å; 1·38 eV.

4.2   0·113 amp/m².

4.3 $A = 7·2 \times 10^5$; amp/m²; $\phi = 4·52$ V.

4.5   Radiation loss $= 8·95 \times 10^5$ watt/m²; evaporation loss $= 1·09 \times 10^{-4}$ watt/m² (hence thermionic emission has a very low thermal efficiency).

4.6   0·013 eV; 48% increase in field.

4.7   4·7 per stage.

5.1 6×10^{15} electrons/sec.

5.2 $3·12 \times 10^7$ m/sec; $1·759 \times 10^{11}$ coul/kg.

5.3 $y^2 = \dfrac{e\,B^2\,Ll}{m\,F\,2}$ where $L =$ distance from deflecting system to end of tube.

5.4 10^{-10} sec.

5.5   vertical 0·98 mm/volt and 0·65 mm/volt
horizontal 1·04 mm/volt and 0·69 mm/volt

5.6 $r = \dfrac{mv}{eB}$; $\omega = \dfrac{eB}{m}$, i.e. independent of radius. Component of v along B unaffected, the motion is spiral.

5.7   The expressions for x and y are the parametric equations for a cycloid.

6.2   1·08 mm.

6.3 $6·9 \times 10^{-9}$ sec.

6.4   The current is thermally limited at 320 mA.

6.5   0·042 weber/m². The working magnetic field in a magnetron is some 50 times this.

7.1   An electron cannot transfer appreciable kinetic energy to a body of greater mass, i.e. a positive ion.

7.2   Below 19·5 eV, no significant energy loss (see 7.1). Above 19·5 eV a helium level is excited by inelastic collision. The level is metastable, and the atom cannot return to the ground state by radiating energy. At 20·5 eV a second level is excited, from which a return to the ground state is possible.

7.3 $1·936 \times 10^6$ m/sec.

7.4   Using the expression $\lambda = 4/\sqrt{2}\pi\ (d_1 + d_2)^2 n$, with $d_2 = 0$, gives $2·68 \times 10^{-5}$ m.

7.5   1·7 cm.

7.6   4 mm; 0·5 mm.

7.7   0·009.

7.8   1 kc/s.

9.1 $E_F = \left(\dfrac{3}{\pi}\right)^{2/3} \left(\dfrac{N}{abc}\right)^{2/3} \dfrac{L^2}{8m}$; $N(E)dE = \dfrac{abc}{4\pi^2}\left(\dfrac{2m}{h^2}\right)^{2/3}\sqrt{E}\,dE$; $\frac{3}{5}\,NE_F$. The reader may find this approach easier to remember and to handle than that given in Section 9.8.

9.2 7·2; 5·7; 12·3 (*N.B.* Aluminium is trivalent). 7·96 × 10⁵; 7·08 × 10⁵; 1·04 × 10⁶ m/sec.

9.3 9·04 × 10²⁶; 2·10 × 10²⁶.

9.4 764°K.

9.6 4·41 m/sec.

10.1 2·3 × 10²⁰ m⁻³ or 1 atom per 3·5 × 10⁸ atoms of Ge: 1·38 × 10¹⁷ m⁻³ or 1 atom per 3·7 × 10¹¹ atoms of Si. This indicates the extremely high limits of purity required in semiconductor work. Compare the densities with those of gases in Question 3.2.

10.2 36 m/sec; 3·6 × 10⁵ m/sec; 1·096 × 10⁵ m/sec. At high fields the drift velocity is no longer small compared with the thermal velocity, and the simple theory breaks down (and Ohm's law with it).

10.3 p-type 2·14 × 10¹⁶ m⁻³ corresponding to 3·39 × 10⁻⁴ mho/cm (intrinsic 3·76 × 10⁻⁴ mho/cm).

10.4 0·78 eV; 1·57 × 10⁻⁶ m (near infrared); 7·3 × 10⁻⁶ m; 5·512 × 10⁻⁷ m (green light).

10.5 The discrepancy on reversing the current arises when the two Hall probes are not exactly in a plane perpendicular to the current flow, and then the 'Hall voltage' will include a contribution from the resistive potential drop along the crystal. 0·725 μV; 1·43 × 10²¹ electrons/m³.

11.1 10⁹ volts/m.

11.2 1·13 × 10⁻⁴ sec; 7.14 × 10⁻⁴ m.

11.5 0·99.

11.7 Note that the donor concentration (which can be varied) controls the breakdown.

11.8 $w = 0.245$ mm.

12.1 $m = -\dfrac{\mu_0 e}{2m}\,G$; $\dfrac{\mu_0 e}{m}\,G$.

12.2 $3N\mu^2/2E_F$.

12.5 0·013 × free electron mass.

13.3 2 × 10¹⁰ m⁻³; a typical value for the E-layer.

14.2 0·03.

Index